W9-AVB-436

DISCARD

THE SIEGE AND FALL OF TROY

ROBERT GRAVES

THE SIEGE AND FALL OF TROY

ILLUSTRATED BY C. WALTER HODGES

DOUBLEDAY & COMPANY, INC.
GARDEN CITY, NEW YORK

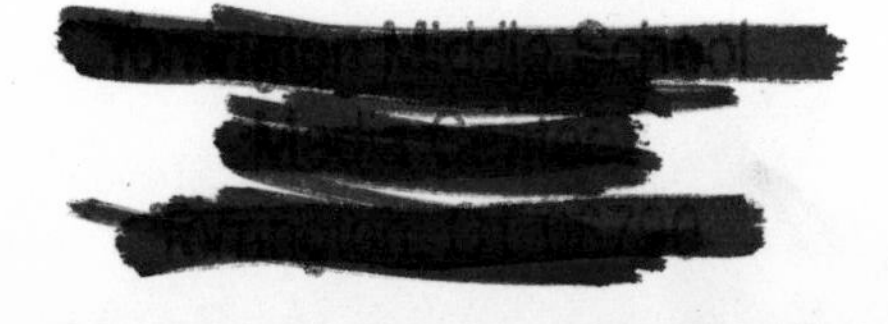

Library of Congress Catalog Card Number 63–16636

Printed in the United States of America
9 8 7 6 5

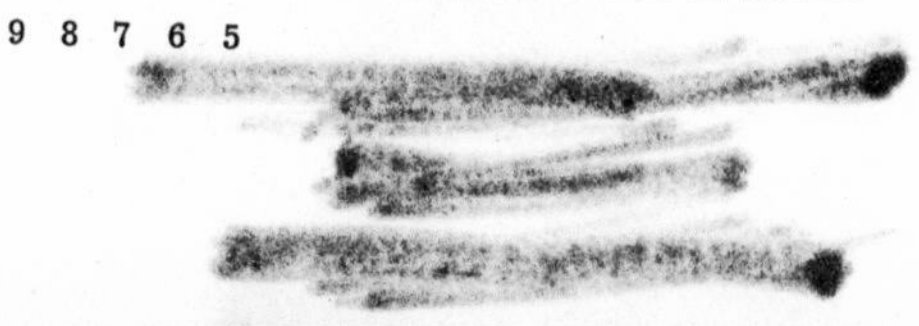

Books for young people
by Robert Graves

THE PENNY FIDDLE

GREEK GODS AND HEROES

THE SIEGE AND FALL OF TROY

CONTENTS

INTRODUCTION

The Siege and Fall of Troy describes all the evils commonly found in war on a large scale—ambition, greed, cruelty, suffering, treachery, incompetence. But the Greeks, though frankly telling how their ancestors ruined themselves in this foolish ten-year-long campaign, did not consider even the Olympian gods blameless. War was forced on King Priam and King Agamemnon, they said, by a jealous quarrel between three goddesses, which Almighty Zeus himself dared not settle: in other words, by forces beyond man's control. The effects were felt as far away as Northern Italy, Libya, Ethiopia, Palestine, Armenia and the Crimea.

Homer's poems are by no means the sole source of the legend; in fact, about two thirds of this book is taken from various other Greek and Latin authors. Yet on linking their accounts together, I am surprised to find how well they agree. A good deal of the story makes historical sense, though Homer borrowed the elopement of Paris and Helen from an earlier Eastern epic, and though the famous wooden horse was, according to some writers, a mere siege-engine—a timber frame covered with horse hides, which allowed Agamemnon's men to scale the walls of Troy at a weak spot. Unfortunately, the adventures of chariot-driving kings and princes are all the fighting that we read about, perhaps because the Homeric minstrels sang their poems at royal courts where democracy was unpopular.

Thersites, the only common soldier mentioned by name in the *Iliad,* is held up for ridicule as an ugly, deformed coward who tries to start a camp mutiny.

Troy, the ruins of which at the entrance of the Hellespont (now the Dardanelles) have been discovered and excavated, fell, it seems, early in the twelfth century B.C. Homer's *Iliad* is now dated at about 750 B.C. The *Odyssey,* though also supposed to be his, was written a generation later by a different hand, and disagrees with the generally accepted Trojan War plot in so far as it whitewashes Odysseus and makes him escape the full punishment he deserved.

English literature, to be properly understood, calls for as close a knowledge of the Trojan War as of the Bible: Helen's beauty, Odysseus's cunning, Hector's noble courage, Achilles's vulnerable heel, Ajax's madness, Agamemnon's murder, have all become proverbial. Yet this is perhaps the first modern attempt to make the whole story, from the foundation of Troy to the return of the victorious Greeks, into a single short book for boys and girls.

Further details, with a list of ancient books consulted, are to be found in my *Greek Myths.*

R.G.

Deyá,
Majorca,
Spain.

THE SIEGE AND FALL OF TROY

ADRIATIC SEA
ILLYRIS
ITALY
Brundisium
CALABRIA
MAC
EPIRUS
THES
DOLOPIANS
Argos
AETOLI
ITHACA
LO
IONIAN SEA
SICILY
Olympia
Sandy Pylos
Methone
GAULUS (Calypso's Island)
MELITA
N
0
50
100
150
200 miles

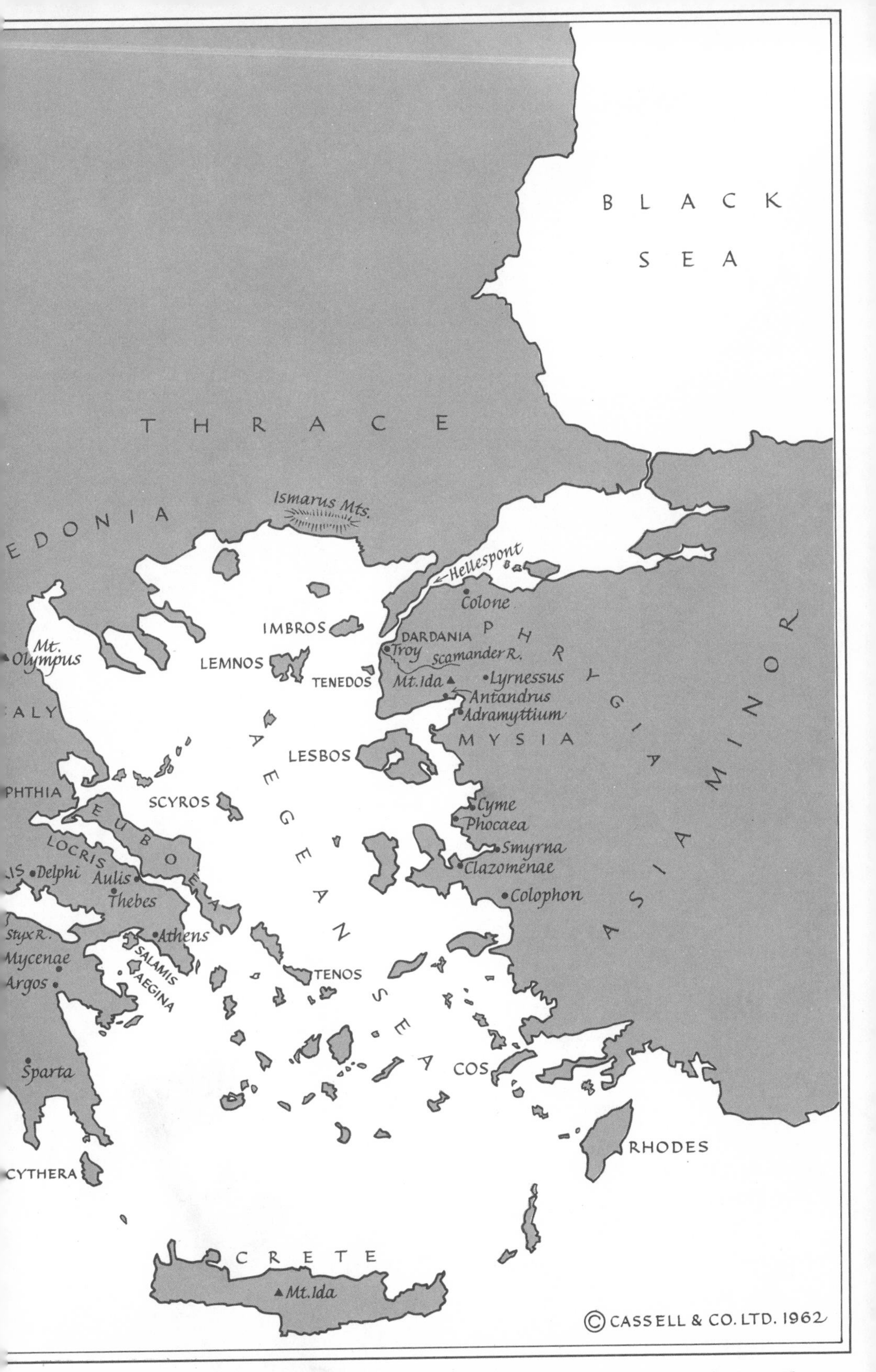

The World of the Greeks and Trojans during the Trojan War

CHAPTER ONE

*

THE FOUNDATION OF TROY

Troy, they say, was founded by Prince Scamander who, because of famine, sailed eastward from the island of Crete with a large number of followers, resolved to plant a colony in some fertile spot. An oracle had ordered him to settle wherever earth-born enemies should disarm his men under cover of darkness. He landed on the coast of Phrygia, within sight of a tall mountain overgrown by pines, which he named Ida in honour of Cretan Mount Ida, and camped beside a river to which he gave his own name, Scamander. On waking next morning, the Cretans saw that a swarm of hungry mice had nibbled their bow-strings, the leather straps of their shields, and all edible parts of their armour. Since these must clearly be the earth-born enemies of the Oracle, Scamander called a halt, made friends with the

Phrygian natives, and began farming the soil. Not long afterwards a colony of Locrian Greeks landed close by and put themselves under his leadership. Though the Phrygians let him build a city near the River Scamander, he could not at first decide on the best position. Then someone proposed sending a dappled cow into the plain, and watching where she lay down to chew her cud. The cow chose a small hill, and around it Scamander's men marked out the boundaries of Troy. They built houses inside, but did not raise the walls for some years, being too busy improving their farms.

At last, a Trojan king named Laomedon won all the help he needed from two important gods—Poseidon and Apollo. They had rebelled against Almighty Zeus, the leading god of Olympus, who sentenced them to be Laomedon's slaves for a whole year. At the King's orders, Poseidon built most of the walls, while Apollo played a harp and looked after the royal flocks and herds. Aeacus, a Locrian colonist, built the wall facing seaward. It was, of course, not nearly so strong as those built by the gods.

Laomedon promised to pay Apollo, Poseidon and Aeacus good wages for their work but, being the meanest of men, sent them off empty-handed. Aeacus sailed back to Greece in disgust; Apollo infected the Trojan flocks with foot-rot; and Poseidon took his revenge by sending a scaly sea-monster ashore to swallow alive every Trojan it came across. When the Trojans blamed Laomedon for their misfortunes, he consulted Apollo's oracle. The priestess told him that the monster would not go away until it had eaten his daughter Hesione. He therefore bound her naked to a rock. In the nick of time, however, the hero Heracles passed, on one of his Labours, and took pity on Hesione. He promised to destroy the monster if Laomedon let him marry her and also gave him two wonderful snow-white horses, a present

from Almighty Zeus. Laomedon eagerly agreed. Heracles thereupon broke the monster's skull with one blow of his olive-wood club, and rescued Hesione.

Laomedon, mean as ever, cheated Heracles: refusing him not only Hesione, but the horses, too. Heracles went away cursing, and returned a few weeks later in command of a small fleet which Aeacus's son Telamon lent him. They took Troy by surprise, shot down Laomedon, killed all his sons—except the youngest, whose name was Priam—and carried off Hesione.

Priam became King of Troy. Having made the city stronger than ever before, after a long and wise reign, he called a council to decide how his sister Hesione could best be brought home. When he suggested sending a fleet to rescue her, the Council advised that he should first politely demand her surrender. Priam's envoys accordingly visited Salamis, where she was said to be living. They were there reminded that Laomedon had originally promised Hesione to Heracles, but cheated him; that Heracles had come back, sacked Troy, carried her off, and given her in marriage to his friend Telamon; that Telamon's father Aeacus had also been cheated by Laomedon; finally that Hesione had borne Telamon a son named Teucer the Archer (now grown up) and did not wish to leave Salamis, even for a short visit.

CHAPTER TWO

*

PARIS AND QUEEN HELEN

King Priam sulked on hearing the envoys' account of their visit to Salamis, and when his own son Paris ran away with Queen Helen of Sparta and brought her to Troy, refused to send her back either. It was this decision that provoked the long, calamitous Trojan War, which benefited nobody, not even the conquerors.

Here is the story of Paris and Helen. Paris was Priam's son by Queen Hecuba who, just before his birth, dreamed that instead of a child she bore a blazing faggot, from which wriggled countless fiery serpents. Priam asked Apollo's prophet Calchas what the dream meant. Calchas answered: 'This child will be Troy's ruin. Cut his throat as soon as he is born!' Priam could not bring himself to kill any baby, especially his own son, but the warning frightened him; so he gave the child to his chief cattleman, saying: 'Leave him behind a bush somewhere in the woods on Mount Ida, and don't go there again for nine days.'

The cattleman obeyed. But on the ninth day, passing through the bushy valley in which Paris had been left, he found a she-bear suckling him. Amazed at this sight, the cattleman brought Paris up with his own children.

Paris grew to be tall, handsome, strong and clever. He was always invited by the other cattlemen to judge bull-fights. Almighty Zeus, watching from his palace on far-off Olympus, noticed how honestly he gave his verdict on such occasions; and one day chose him to preside over a beauty contest at which he did not care to appear himself. This is what had happened. The Goddess of Quarrels, Eris by name, was not invited to a famous wedding (that of the Sea-goddess Thetis and King Peleus of Phthia), attended by all the other gods and goddesses. Eris spitefully threw a golden apple among the guests, after scratching on the peel: 'For the Most Beautiful!' They would have handed the apple to Thetis, as the bride; but were afraid of offending the three far more important goddesses present: Hera, Almighty Zeus's wife; Athene, his unmarried daughter, who was Goddess not only of Wisdom but of Battle; and his daughter-in-law Aphrodite, Goddess of Love. Each of them thought herself the most beautiful, and they began quarreling about the apple, as Eris had intended. Zeus's one hope of domestic peace lay in ordering a beauty contest and choosing an honest judge.

So Hermes, Herald of the Gods, flew down with the golden apple and a message for Paris from Zeus. 'Three goddesses,' he announced, 'will visit you here on Mount Ida, and Almighty Zeus's orders are that you shall award this apple to the most beautiful. They will all, of course, abide by your decision.' Paris disliked the task, but could not avoid it.

The goddesses arrived together, each in turn unveiling her beauty; and each in turn offering a bribe. Hera undertook to make Paris Emperor of Asia. Athene undertook to make him the wisest man alive and victorious in all his battles. But Aphrodite sidled up, saying: 'Darling Paris, I declare that you're the handsomest young fellow I've seen for years! Why waste your time here among bulls and cows and stupid cattlemen? Why not move to some rich city and lead a more interesting life? You deserve to marry a woman almost as beautiful as myself—let me suggest Queen Helen of Sparta. One look at you, and I'll make her fall so deep in love that she won't mind leaving her husband, her palace, her family—everything, for your sake!' Excited by Aphrodite's account of Helen's beauty, Paris handed her the apple; whereupon Hera and Athene went off angrily, arm in arm, to plot the destruction of the whole Trojan race.

Next day, Paris paid his first visit to Troy, and found an athletic festival in progress. His foster-father, the cattleman, who had come too, advised him against entering the boxing contest which was staged in front of Priam's throne; but Paris stepped forward and won the crown of victory by sheer courage rather than skill. He put his name down for the foot-race, too, and ran first. When Priam's sons challenged him to a longer race, he beat them again. They grew so annoyed, to think that a mere peasant had carried off three crowns of victory in a row, that they drew their swords. Paris ran for protection to the altar of Zeus, while his foster-father fell on his knees before Priam, crying: 'Your Majesty, pardon me! This is your lost son.'

The King summoned Hecuba, and Paris's foster-father showed her a rattle left in his hands when he was a baby.

She knew it at once; so they took Paris with them to the palace, and there celebrated a huge banquet in honour of his return. Nevertheless, Calchas and the other priests of Apollo warned Priam that unless Paris were immediately put to death, Troy would go up in smoke. He answered: 'Better that Troy should burn, than that my wonderful son should die!'

Priam made ready a fleet to sail for Salamis and rescue Queen Hesione by force of arms. Paris offered to take command, adding: 'And if we can't bring my aunt home, perhaps I may capture some Greek princess whom we can hold as a hostage.' He was of course already planning to carry off Helen, and had no intention of fetching back his old aunt, in whom no Trojan but Priam took the least interest, and who felt perfectly happy at Salamis.

While Priam was deciding whether he should give Paris the command, Menelaus, King of Sparta, happened to visit Troy on some business matter. He made friends with Paris and invited him to Sparta; which enabled Paris to carry out his plan easily, using no more than a single fast ship. He and Menelaus sailed as soon as the wind blew favourably and, on arrival at Sparta, feasted together nine days running. Under Aphrodite's spell, Helen loved Paris at first sight, but was greatly embarrassed by his bold behaviour. He even dared to write 'I love Helen!' in wine spilt on the top of the banqueting table. Yet Menelaus, grieved by news of his father's death in Crete, noticed nothing; and when the nine days ended, he set sail for the funeral, leaving Helen to rule in his absence. This was no more than Helen's due, since he had become King of Sparta by marrying her.

That same night Helen and Paris eloped in his fast ship, putting aboard most of the palace treasures that she had inherited from her foster-father. And Paris stole a great mass of gold out of Apollo's temple, in revenge for the prophecy made by his priests that he should be killed at birth. Hera spitefully raised a heavy storm, which blew their ship to Cyprus; and Paris decided to stay there some months before he went home—Menelaus might be anchored off Troy, waiting to catch him. In Cyprus, where he had friends, he collected a fleet to raid Sidon, a rich city on the coast of Palestine. The raid was a great success: Paris killed the Sidonian king, and captured vast quantities of treasure.

When at last he returned to Troy, his ship loaded with silver, gold and precious stones, the Trojans welcomed him rapturously. Everyone thought Helen so beautiful, beyond all comparison, that King Priam himself swore never to give her up, even in exchange for his sister Hesione. Paris quieted his enemies, the Trojan priests of Apollo, by handing them the gold robbed from the God's treasury at Sparta; and almost the only two people who took a gloomy view of what would now happen were Paris's sister Cassandra, and her twin-brother Helenus, both of whom possessed the gift of prophecy. This they had won accidentally, while still children, by falling asleep in Apollo's temple. The sacred serpents had come up and licked their ears, which enabled them to hear the God's secret voice. Yet it did them no good: because Apollo arranged that no one would believe their prophecies. Time after time Cassandra and Helenus had warned Priam never to let Paris visit Greece. Now they warned him to send Helen and her treasure back at once if he wanted to avoid a long and terrible war. Priam paid not the least attention.

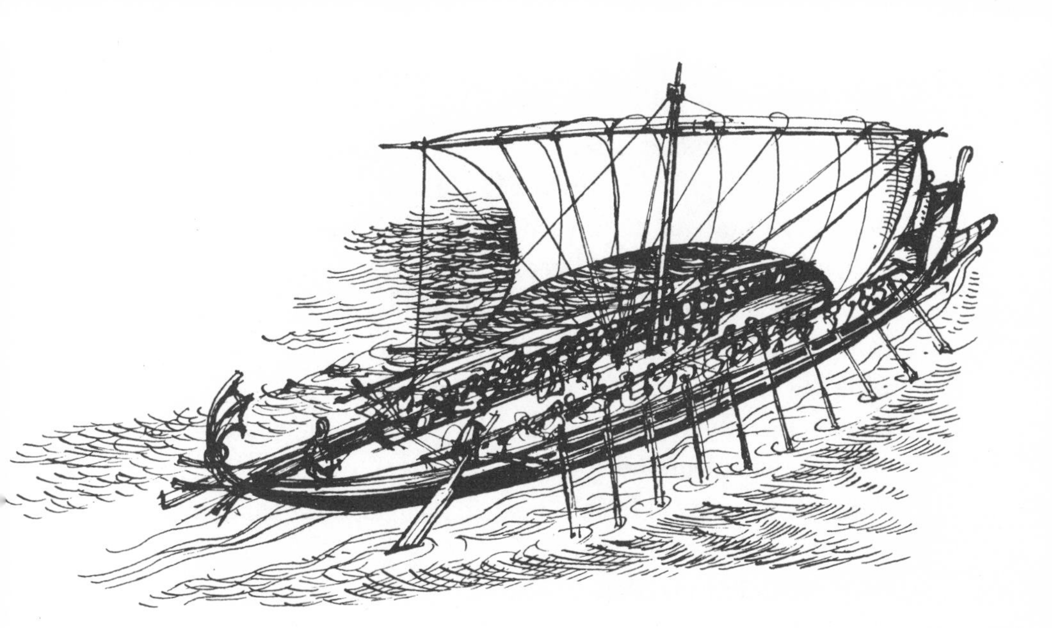

CHAPTER THREE

*

THE EXPEDITION SAILS

When Helen had grown to womanhood at Sparta, in the palace of her foster-father Tyndareus—she was the daughter of Almighty Zeus by Leda, Queen of Sparta, and sister of the Heavenly Twins Castor and Polydeuces—most of the kings and princes of Greece wanted to marry her. Among them were Diomedes of Argos, Idomeneus of Crete, Cinyras of Cyprus, Patroclus of Phthia, Palamedes of Euboea, Ajax of Salamis, his half-brother Teucer the Archer (Hesione's Greek son), and Odysseus of Ithaca. They all brought rich presents, or all except Odysseus. Having no hope of success, he came empty-handed. The husband chosen would obviously be Menelaus, brother of the High King Agamemnon of Mycenae, who had married Helen's sister Clytaemnestra.

Though Tyndareus sent none of these suitors away, he dared not accept their presents for fear he might be accused of favouritism. But since each had set his heart on winning Helen, the loveliest in Greece, Tyndareus grew frightened at the prospect of an open battle in his palace. Odysseus came to him, saying: 'If I tell you how to avoid a fight, King Tyndareus, may I marry your niece Penelope?' 'It's a bargain!' Tyndareus cried. 'Very well,' said Odysseus. 'This is what you must do: make them swear to defend whoever becomes Helen's husband against everyone else who grudges him his good luck.'

'What sensible advice!' said Tyndareus, smiling gratefully. He at once sacrificed a horse to Poseidon, cut the carcase into twelve pieces, and made each suitor stand on one of them, repeating after him the oath suggested by Odysseus. Then he buried the pieces beneath a mound called 'The Horse's Tomb'; and explained that the men who broke his oath would fall under the God's lasting displeasure. Afterwards he announced that Menelaus was to be Helen's husband, and named him heir to the Spartan throne.

If Hera and Athene had not been so vexed with Paris for awarding the apple to Aphrodite, the Trojan War might never have begun. But as soon as Hera heard that he was carrying off Helen (who, by the way, left behind her nine-year-old daughter Hermione), she sent Iris, Goddess of the Rainbow, to tell Menelaus the news. Menelaus hurried home from Crete, complaining to his brother Agamemnon: 'That rascal Paris came to Sparta as a guest, and has wickedly eloped with my wife Helen. He envied my good luck. I count on you to remind all her other suitors of the oath that they swore before Poseidon. They must join us at once in an expedition against Troy.'

Agamemnon, knowing that Troy was an almost impregnable city and that King Priam had powerful allies in Asia Minor and Thrace, hesitated for a while. Then he said: 'Yes, I fear we may have to do as you ask, brother. But first let us send envoys to Troy, demanding the return of Helen and the stolen treasure. If Priam is sensible, he will surely not risk a war against Greece.'

When Agamemnon's envoys came to Troy, Priam told them that he knew nothing of the matter—which was true, because Paris had not yet got back from Sidon. He added: 'Nevertheless, my lords, if Queen Helen has really left Sparta with my son and the Palace treasures, she must have done so of her own free will. Paris took only a single ship, and his few sailors can hardly have plundered King Menelaus's palace, and Apollo's temple, without her help.'

This reasonable answer annoyed Agamemnon, who sent messengers throughout Greece, to remind Helen's suitors of their oath and collect volunteers. 'The Gods are on our side,' he explained, 'because of Paris's treacherous behaviour. We shall have no trouble in storming Troy, which is immensely rich. Its fall will give us passage into the Black Sea. The Trojans, on guard at the straits, now make us pay double for all imported Eastern goods, such as timber, iron, hides, perfumes, spices and precious stones. How pleasant to save so much money!'

Agamemnon and Palamedes visited Odysseus, King of Ithaca, but found him most unwilling to join the expedition. In fact, when told of their arrival, he put on a prophet's round felt cap, then ploughed a field with an ox and an ass yoked together, flinging salt over his shoulder as he went. He did this because an oracle had warned him that, having once left Ithaca to fight at Troy, he would not return until twenty years later—alone and in rags. To 'plough with an ox and an ass' was a proverb meaning to work summer and winter; and each furrow sown with salt stood for a wasted year. But as soon as the plough reached the tenth furrow Palamedes snatched Odysseus's son Telemachus from Penelope's arms, and set him down in front of the team, forcing his father to pull up. Palamedes thereby prophesied that *Telemachus,* or 'the final battle', would take place in the tenth year. Unable to deny this, Odysseus promised to contribute a small fleet.

Agamemnon's envoys also went to Cyprus where King Cinyras promised fifty ships, but cheated by sending only one real ship and forty-nine toy ones, with dolls for crews, which the captain launched as he drew near the coast of Greece. Agamemnon called on Apollo to punish the fraud; and Apollo made Cinyras die of a sudden illness.

Calchas, the Trojan priest of Apollo, consulting the Delphic oracle at Priam's suggestion, was ordered by the priestess to join the Greeks and not let them abandon their siege of Troy whatever might happen. He now prophesied that Troy could not be taken without the help of a young hero named Achilles, son of King Peleus and the Sea-goddess Thetis, at whose wedding the fateful apple had been thrown. Thetis soon tired of her mortal husband, because he grew older, feebler and more boring every day; while she, as a goddess, always stayed young and lively. But she decided to make their son Achilles invulnerable by dipping him in the holy river Styx, held tight by one heel; and afterwards brought him to Cheiron the Centaur—these Centaurs were half men, half horses—where he got the best possible education: in riding, hunting, fighting, music, medicine and history. Achilles killed his first wild boar as soon as he could walk, and a little later ran fast enough to overtake and capture stags. Being the son of a goddess, he was fully grown at an age when other children still clung to their mothers' skirts.

The Fate-goddesses had told Thetis that if her son went to Troy, he would never return alive: his destiny was either a long, quiet life, or a short, exciting, glorious one. So, guessing that Odysseus would try to recruit Achilles for the war, she took him away from Cheiron and sent him to the island of Scyros. There he lived among the king's daughters disguised as a girl.

Odysseus heard a rumour of Achilles's whereabouts, and sailed to Scyros with a chestful of valuable jewels and clothes as gifts for the princesses. When they all gathered around and made their choice, Odysseus ordered his trumpeter to blow an alarm at the palace gate. One of the girls immediately stripped off her linen tunic and seized the shield and sword which lay in the chest beside other gifts. This girl was of course Achilles, whom Odysseus now easily persuaded to join the expedition. King Peleus gave Achilles command of a small fleet, though insisting that he was too young to go to war without his tutor—a wise old man named Phoenix, King of the Dolopians. Achilles's inseparable companion, his cousin Patroclus, came too; but, having been one of Helen's suitors, he would have gone in any case. Peleus counted on Patroclus to guard Achilles in battle; and on Phoenix to give him good advice.

The Greek fleet gathered at Aulis, a protected beach opposite the island of Euboea. Over a thousand ships, holding about thirty men each, were drawn up on the white sand—some brought from as far away as North-Western Greece and the islands of Cos, Rhodes and Crete.

Agamemnon, the Commander-in-Chief, sacrificed a hundred bulls to Almighty Zeus and to Apollo, but no sooner had he done so than a blue serpent with blood-red markings darted from behind the altar and made for a plane-tree growing near by. A sparrow had built her nest on the highest branch, and in it were eight little sparrows. The serpent ate them all, one by one; then ate the mother too. Calchas read this as a sign that though nine years must pass before Troy would fall, fall it would at last.

The immense fleet steered for Troy, using oars and sails, but Aphrodite sent a storm from the north-east to blow it off course. On reaching Asia Minor, the Greeks plundered the countryside, which they supposed to be part of Phrygia. They were, really, in Mysia, a long way to the south. A hard battle against the Mysians cost them two or three hundred men before their mistake was discovered. When they put to sea again, Aphrodite scattered the fleet with a fearful storm, and the ships that stayed afloat struggled back to Aulis as best they could. One third of the expedition had been lost.

Agamemnon grew restless. The winds were still unfavourable, and provisions running short. He consulted Calchas. Now, unless Calchas happened to be prophetically inspired by Apollo, he was in the habit of making wild guesses. On this occasion he said: 'My lord King, Artemis is angry because, when you were hunting a few days ago and shot a stag through the neck, at a great distance, you foolishly boasted: "Artemis herself could not have done better!"' 'What must I do to appease the Goddess?' Agamemnon asked. 'Sacrifice the most beautiful of your daughters to her,' Calchas answered. 'You mean Iphigeneia?' cried Agamemnon. 'But my wife Clytaemnestra would never allow it!' 'Then why tell her?' asked Calchas. 'I refuse to sacrifice my daughter!' were Agamemnon's parting words.

When the Greek leaders learned that the expedition was held up because their Commander-in-Chief would not lis-

ten to Apollo's own prophet, some of them wanted to depose him in favour of Prince Palamedes of Euboea; and Odysseus warned Agamemnon what was happening. So, after all, a royal herald went to fetch Iphigeneia from Mycenae, on the lying excuse, invented by Odysseus, that Agamemnon wanted to reward Achilles for his brave deeds in Mysia by making her his wife. Although Agamemnon sent a secret message to Clytaemnestra: 'Disregard the herald!', it never reached her. Menelaus had intercepted the message, and Iphigeneia presently arrived at Aulis.

Achilles, hearing that Iphigeneia had been lured to death by a mischievous use of his name, protested angrily, and tried to save her life. However, she nobly consented to die for the sake of Greece, and offered her young neck to the sacrificial axe. But before the blade could fall, a peal of thunder rang out, lightning flashed, and Iphigeneia vanished. Artemis had snatched her away through the air, to a distant peninsula now called the Crimea, where she became priestess to the savage Taurians.

The north-easterly gale dropped, and the huge fleet once more steered for Troy.

CHAPTER FOUR

*

THE FIRST EIGHT YEARS OF WAR

The Greeks landed on Tenedos, an island visible from Troy, and sacked the city. It was here that an accident happened to King Philoctetes of Methone, who had inherited Heracles's famous bow and arrows. As he was offering a huge sacrifice to Apollo, in gratitude for the victory that his troops had just won, a poisonous serpent bit him on the heel. No salves or fomentations could reduce the swelling. The wound smelt so horrible and Philoctetes howled so miserably that, after a few days, Agamemnon could stand it no longer. He took Philoctetes away, in a small boat, to a rocky island near Lemnos, and there put him ashore. Philoctetes's wound continued to cause him intense pain, but he kept alive by eating the roots and seeds of asphodel and by shooting wild birds.

Before leaving Tenedos, Agamemnon sent Menelaus, Odysseus and Palamedes on a mission to King Priam, threatening to level Troy with the ground, unless he gave up Helen and all the stolen treasure, besides paying a vast sum in gold to cover the expenses already incurred. Priam and most other Trojans had no intention of surrendering Helen, or of paying for the wrecked ships. Only one member of the Royal Council, Antenor, who had been Priam's envoy to Greece when he demanded the return of Hesione, and whose wife Theano acted as Athene's priestess at Troy, dared say that Helen should, in justice, be restored to her husband. The Council shouted him down; but at least he prevented them from murdering Agamemnon's envoys. The fact was that the love-magic with which Aphrodite invested Helen had so strong an effect on almost every man in the city, including old King Priam himself, that they would cheerfully have faced torture for one smile from her lovely lips.

When the Greeks sailed against Troy at dawn, two days later, the Trojans flocked to the beach, where they shot arrows and flung showers of stones to prevent the ships from landing. Calchas had prophesied that the first man ashore would die after a short but glorious fight; and even Achilles hesitated to risk his life. Only Protesilaus the Thessalian dared defy fate. He leaped from his ship and killed a number of Trojans, before Priam's son Hector speared him. Protesilaus had recently married, and his wife hearing in a dream that he was dead, prayed Persephone, Goddess of Death, to let him visit her for no longer than three hours. Persephone granted the prayer, and released Protesilaus on parole. After three hours' loving talk with him, his wife killed herself, and they went down, hand in hand, to the gloomy Underworld.

Achilles waited until the last. He then took such a prodigious jump that a spring of water burst out where his feet struck Trojan soil. Cycnus, son of Poseidon, whose body was proof against stones and weapons, led the Trojans at this point, and had been killing Greeks by the score. Achilles, equally invulnerable, tried to spear Cycnus or cut off his head; but in vain. Finally he battered at Cycnus's face with the sword-hilt, made him trip backwards over a rock, then knelt on his chest and strangled him with his helmet strap.

The Trojans fled when they saw Cycnus lying there lifeless; and the Greeks, having scuttled the main Trojan fleet, which lay moored at the river mouth, hauled their own ships high up on the beach, and built a stockade of pine logs around them. Next day they paraded in long lines and marched to the attack; but found the city gates so well guarded, and the walls so enormous and well manned, that they suffered heavy losses and were forced to retire. After three more unsuccessful attempts, Agamemnon called a Royal Council, at which it was decided to starve Troy out. This plan, too, proved difficult. He had not brought enough men to protect his fleet and at the same time keep a ring of armed camps around the city capable of resisting a mass enemy attack. Every night the Trojans brought in food and supplies by the gates on the landward side, and the Greeks stayed helplessly where they had disembarked.

At another Council meeting, Odysseus spoke up plainly. 'Calchas was right,' he said. 'The war will last for years, but we're bound to be victorious in the end. This is like a battle between a lion and a sea-monster: although we Greeks have won command of the sea, the Trojans still have command of the land. I suggest that we sit in our stockade, sending out ships to raid all the islands and cities allied to

King Priam. We shall thus both keep ourselves in food and weaken the enemy. Since Priam can't protect his allies without a fleet, they'll desert him one by one. And I suggest that Prince Achilles shall lead these expeditions.'

The Council agreed. Eight years were therefore spent by the Greeks in a siege that was not really a siege and grew more tedious year after year. They longed to see their sweethearts or wives and children again; and the shoddy huts which they had built in rows behind the stockade could never become proper homes. Quarrels sprang up for small, foolish reasons, and often led to murder. Yet if a soldier dared say that peace must be made on any terms, he was called a coward and ordered to risk his life in the next raid.

Great Ajax of Salamis, Telamon's son, twice landed in Thrace and fetched back a heap of treasure. But most of the raids were led by Achilles, who sacked some thirty cities up and down the coast of Asia Minor, among them Lesbos, Phocaea, Colophon, Smyrna, Clazomenae, Cyme, Aegialus, Tenos, Adramyttium, Colone, Antandrus, and Hypoplacian Thebes, where he killed Hector's father-in-law and seven of his brothers-in-law. The captives from Thebes included a beautiful girl named Chryseis, daughter of Chryses, a priest of Apollo, who happened to have gone there on a visit. This Chryseis later caused the angry dispute between Agamemnon and Achilles which nearly brought the Greeks to disaster.

Achilles also attacked Dardanus, a city not far from Troy. It was ruled by Aeneas, a cousin of King Priam, in the name of his aged father Anchises. Since, for some reason or other, Priam treated Aeneas coldly, although his cousin and the son of Aphrodite herself, the Dardanians had remained neutral. Achilles, not respecting Aeneas's neutrality, chased him down the wooded slopes of Ida, drove off his cattle, killed his herdsmen, and sacked Lyrnessus, the city in which he took refuge. Aeneas was rescued by Almighty Zeus; but Achilles's behaviour so angered him that he went over to the Trojans, and fought bravely for them—helped by his mother Aphrodite.

A quarrel with far-reaching results now broke out between Palamedes of Euboea and Odysseus. Palamedes had invented lighthouses, scales, weights and measures, the alphabet, discus-throwing, and the art of posting sentinels. Odysseus grew jealous of his genius. When one day Agamemnon sent Odysseus on a raid against Thrace, in search of corn, he returned empty-handed, and Palamedes laughed at him for his lack of success. 'It was not my fault,' said Odysseus. 'There happened to be no corn in any of the cities I attacked. You would have done no better.' 'Are you sure?' asked Palamedes. He set sail at once and, a few days later, brought in a whole shipload of grain.

'How did you succeed?' Odysseus asked.

'By using my common sense,' was the only answer Palamedes gave him.

Odysseus decided to get his own back and, after brooding awhile, hit on a wicked plan. He came into Agamemnon's hut early one morning. 'The gods,' he said, 'have warned me in a dream that a traitor is hidden among us. They say that the camp must be moved for twenty-four hours.'

Agamemnon gave the necessary orders, and that evening Odysseus secretly buried a sack of gold at the spot where Palamedes's hut had stood. Then he forced a Phrygian prisoner to write a letter in his own language, as if from King Priam to Palamedes. It read: 'The gold which I send you herewith is the price agreed between us for your drugging of the Greek sentries. My son, Prince Hector, will be ready to break into the naval camp at dawn, in three days' time.' Odysseus told the prisoner to hand Palamedes this letter, but had him killed as he went off. When the camp was moved back again, someone noticed the prisoner's body, and took the letter to Agamemnon's Council. An interpreter read it to them, and Palamedes was at once accused of treason. When he denied accepting any gold from Priam, Odysseus suggested a thorough search of his hut. The gold was found under the tent-pole and Agamemnon, who hated Palamedes because he had been the army's choice for Commander-in-Chief at Aulis, sentenced him to death by stoning.

On his way to the place of execution, Palamedes cried aloud: 'Truth, I lament your fate! You have died before me.' He had earned general gratitude by inventing dice, made from knuckle-bones of sheep, which helped to amuse the bored and homesick soldiers. But Odysseus convinced them that he was a traitor.

The news reached Palamedes's father Nauplius, King of Euboea, who came to Troy in a rage, protesting that his son had been the victim of a vile plot. Agamemnon roughly sent him away. 'Palamedes,' he said, 'was fairly tried and justly condemned.' Nauplius swore vengeance, withdrew his ships and men from the camp, and when he got home again, went around Greece visiting the wives of all Palamedes's enemies in turn, and making each of them believe the same story: 'Your husband has captured a lovely slave-girl. He intends to divorce you and marry her instead.' A few of these unhappy queens committed suicide; but the rest revenged themselves by taking lovers—such as Clytaemnestra, Agamemnon's wife; and the wife of Diomedes, King of Argos; and the wife of Idomeneus the Cretan; and (some say) Penelope, Odysseus's wife—plotting to kill their husbands when they returned.

Achilles's anger against Agamemnon grew hotter. Besides being convinced of Palamedes's innocence, he hated the High King's unfair way of distributing captured treasure. Instead of letting the leader of a raid keep two-thirds of the treasure for himself and his men, and giving the rest to a common fund, Agamemnon had it all distributed among the Councillors according to their rank. This meant that if a hundredweight of gold were brought in, Agamemnon would claim ten pounds; Idomeneus eight; Menelaus, Nestor, Diomedes and Odysseus five each; and so on; whereas Achilles himself, or Great Ajax, being a mere prince, not a king, could claim only a single pound—unless the Council were pleased to vote him a small extra prize of honour. Achilles felt cheated because none of these kings except Odysseus ever went on raids, thinking it beneath their dignity. Yet the Council refused to alter its rule.

Just outside Troy stood a temple of Apollo, which Greeks and Trojans had agreed to treat as neutral ground. One morning, when Achilles went there unarmed to offer a sacrifice, he unexpectedly ran into Queen Hecuba, accompanied by her beautiful daughter Polyxena, who was dressed in scarlet linen and wore a heavy gold necklace. Achilles at once fell violently in love. He said nothing at the time, but returned to camp in a torment, and presently sent his charioteer back to the temple, knowing that Hector would be sacrificing that same afternoon. The charioteer was to ask Hector privately: 'On what terms may Prince Achilles hope to marry your sister Polyxena?' Hector, though enraged because Achilles had killed his father-in-law and his seven brothers-in-law, put the good of Troy before any private grudge. He gave the charioteer a sealed letter addressed to Achilles, which read: 'I hear, Prince, that King Agamemnon and his Council have insulted you on many occasions. Not being his subject, but a volunteer, and also too young to have been one of Queen Helen's suitors, you may perhaps feel inclined to act in your own interests—by admitting me and my men into the Greek camp one night. When we have killed King Agamemnon and his brother Menelaus, my sister Polyxena will be yours to marry.'

Achilles seriously considered this offer, but feared that if he let the Trojans into the camp, some of his friends (such as his cousins Great and Little Ajax) might be killed by mistake. So he decided to wait until Troy fell, and then win Polyxena without having to make Hector any payment.

CHAPTER FIVE

*

ACHILLES QUARRELS WITH AGAMEMNON

By the beginning of the fateful ninth year, Troy herself had suffered little, but many of her allies had deserted, and others could be kept loyal only with huge bribes of gold. Priam's treasury was almost exhausted. Nevertheless, no city or tribe in Asia Minor wanted the Greeks to defeat the Trojans and enrich themselves by controlling the Black Sea trade; so when news spread that a Greek attack on Troy was planned for the early summer, large forces came to help King Priam from far-off Lycia, Paphlagonia, and elsewhere.

Almighty Zeus found himself in an awkward position. Priam had always given him splendid sacrifices, and the Trojans were behaving bravely and honourably, which was more than might be said of the Greeks. Zeus could not deny having arranged the beauty contest, and knew well that the irresistible Love-goddess Aphrodite had arranged the scandalous love-affair between Paris and Helen which was the cause of war. Yet he dared not antagonize his wife Hera and his daughter Athene, both of whom demanded vengeance on Troy. So he stayed neutral, though making things as unpleasant as possible for the Greeks.

It will be remembered that Achilles took prisoner the lovely Chryseis, daughter of Apollo's priest Chryses. In the distribution of spoils she went to Agamemnon as his slave, and grew quite fond of him; but one day Chryses suddenly walked into the Greek camp, carrying a gold wand bound with a woollen head-band sacred to Apollo, and demanded Chryseis's return, offering a large ransom for her. Although the Royal Council urged Agamemnon to agree, he flew into a great rage, telling Chryses roughly to begone and never again show his face there, unless he wanted a severe beating. 'Chryseis is mine,' he shouted, 'and I don't intend to give her up!'

Chryses withdrew and, standing by the seashore, prayed to Apollo for vengeance. Apollo ran down angrily from Olympus, a silver bow in his hand, and arrows rattling in his quiver. He sat on a near-by hill and began to shoot at the Greeks. Every arrow was tipped with plague, and since they kept their camp in a filthy state, seldom troubling to cart away the refuse, or wash themselves, or change their clothes, plague spread quickly from man to man. Before ten days had passed, hundreds were dead, and their comrades found it more and more difficult to burn the corpses—the supply of wood was giving out. This calamity alarmed Hera, who visited Achilles in a dream. 'Prince,' she said, 'call a Royal Council at once, and see what you can do to save the expedition.'

Achilles did as she ordered him, and when the Council met, suggested that Agamemnon should ask some reliable prophet why Apollo had sent the plague. Calchas was called upon. He rose and said: 'If I tell you the truth, my lords, and if it displeases the High King, who will protect me against his anger?'

'I will, for one,' said Achilles. 'Rely on me!'

Calchas then told the Council bluntly that, unless Chryseis were restored to her father without a ransom, the plague would continue till no Greek survived.

Agamemnon called Calchas a liar. 'It's a spiteful trick,' he burst out, 'to rob me of Chryseis—whom, by the way, I far prefer to my wife Clytaemnestra, and who has been given me by the Royal Council as a prize of honour. Nevertheless, I will surrender her, if you insist on believing this improbable story—but on condition that I'm compensated for my loss with an equally beautiful and talented slave-girl.'

Achilles lost his temper, too, calling Agamemnon a greedy rascal. 'You know well enough,' he said, 'that there's no common stock of booty to draw from. Everything has been distributed as soon as it came in—most unfairly, too! And which of us will be asked to give you his own beautiful slave—that's what I want to know?'

'Hold your tongue!' cried Agamemnon. 'I daresay you hope to keep your own prize of honour while I, though High King and Commander-in-Chief of the Greeks, go empty-handed? This Council must do as I ask or I shall take the law into my hands and choose the prize of honour that pleases me—from whoever happens to possess the slave I need: whether Great Ajax, or Odysseus, or even yourself. But meanwhile, I suppose, Chryseis must be sent back to her father.'

Achilles grew angrier than ever. 'I, for one, am not under your orders!' he shouted. 'I came here as a volunteer. Moreover, my men and I have so far done most of the fighting and been given the meanest possible share of the spoils. You threaten to seize the prize which the Council voted me after my sack of Hypoplacian Thebes? Then I have no intention of humbling myself any longer by further thankless efforts to fill your private treasury! I'm sailing home.'

'So be it,' said Agamemnon. 'Obviously, you're a coward as well as a traitor. Sail home, if you must, but I swear by Almighty Zeus that I'll first visit your hut and take away your slave Briseis, using force if necessary! That'll teach you never to argue with your elders and betters.'

Achilles half-drew his sword from its sheath, and would have killed Agamemnon on the spot, had Athene not seen that this might provoke a civil war in the Greek camp and save Troy from destruction. She appeared suddenly at Achilles's side, unseen to all except him, and restrained his hand. 'Call Agamemnon what names you please,' she said, 'but use no violence! I solemnly swear that, before many days have gone by, Agamemnon will beg your pardon and offer you treasures enormously more valuable than your Theban slave.'

Achilles pushed the sword back into its sheath, muttering: 'It's always wise to obey the immortal gods.' Then he turned to Agamemnon, throwing at him every ugly name in the Greek language, and saying how surprised he was that no other member of the Council dared stand up to him. The time must come, he said, when the Greeks, on the point of being massacred by Hector's Trojans, would beg him to save their lives; but he would grimly fold his arms and watch while Agamemnon writhed in despair and cursed his own greed and stubbornness.

Old Nestor tried unsuccessfully to patch the quarrel. The Council dispersed and Agamemnon, having sent Chryseis home by sea, under Odysseus's charge, called his two royal heralds and said: 'Fetch me the slave Briseis from Achilles's hut.'

They went off in fear of their lives, but Achilles, who trusted Athene's oath, did not resist them. He only repeated his warning of what would happen when Hector attacked the Greek camp. After striding along the seashore, plunged in gloom, he stopped and prayed for help to his mother, the Sea-goddess Thetis. She swam up from her underwater cave, sat on the sand, and listened sympathetically as he told her his troubles; then promised to visit Almighty Zeus and make him punish Agamemnon.

That afternoon Hera saw Thetis in earnest conversation with Zeus, and at suppertime asked him what their talk had been about. He refused to answer, and when Hera snapped: 'I suppose she was asking a favour for her son Achilles—to let Hector give the Greeks a severe beating?' threatened to thrash her black and blue. Hera dared say no more, and her son Hephaestus the Smith, Aphrodite's lame husband, hurriedly brought her a cup of sweet wine. 'Please don't nag,' he muttered. 'Father Zeus is quite capable of hurling his thunderbolt at us, and then where should we be? Drink this, dear mother!'

Zeus decided to keep the promise he had made Thetis, by sending down a False Dream, disguised as old King Nestor. That night, the False Dream told Agamemnon: 'A message from Almighty Zeus. He's been persuaded by Queen Hera to let you capture Troy. Parade your troops at dawn, and advance!'

Agamemnon immediately roused his Council and reported the message. Old Nestor, proud to have figured in a divine dream, thought it must be authentic, and advised instant obedience. But Agamemnon called a General Assembly of all his troops, and very foolishly decided to test their courage by reminding them how few they were compared with the Trojans, how long the war had lasted, and how little hope they had of victory. 'Why fight against fate?' he asked them. 'Perhaps after all we should sail home, before worse befalls us?'

Instead of everyone protesting loudly, as he hoped, and crying: 'No, no, we've sworn to take Troy!' there came shouts of: 'Well said, well said, your Majesty! Let's set sail at once!'

Hera heard the jubilant shouts, the trampling of feet, and the noise of ships being loaded. She hurriedly sent Athene down to correct the High King's mistake. Athene saw Odysseus standing glumly beside his vessel, and told him to use Agamemnon's sceptre for taming the men into obedience. He did so, and kept them from launching their ships, by a threat that anyone who took Agamemnon's joke seriously and tried to sail off, would be executed as a deserter. He then called another General Assembly, which he reminded of Calchas's prophecy about the serpent and the sparrows, at the same time mentioning Agamemnon's divine dream. 'Let's eat a good breakfast, comrades,' he said, 'and then we'll attack Troy, which is bound to fall. Almighty Zeus has promised us that!'

A common soldier named Thersites, the ugliest man in the army—bandy-legged, hunch-backed, and almost bald, stood yelling abuse at the Greek leaders: 'Why should we stay here and suffer for a pack of greedy, cowardly kings? Look at the mean way Agamemnon has treated Achilles: all he wants is loot and glory, at other people's expense! Why don't we go home, as he suggested, and let him carry on this war alone?'

Odysseus walked up to Thersites and cried: 'Silence, you miserable windbag! I won't allow you to insult our great Commander-in-Chief.' Then he beat Thersites with the heavy golden sceptre until tears rolled down his cheeks.

Thersites had such a nasty tongue and so many enemies that all present cheered Odysseus uproariously and, after a good meal of beef roasted on spits, and copious draughts of rich Lemnian wine, the entire army, except Achilles's Myrmidons, formed up for battle. The Trojans, watching from the high walls, hastily put on their armour, harnessed their chariots, opened the City gates, and swarmed out to meet the attack. Great clouds of dust arose on both sides of the plain, darkening the sun.

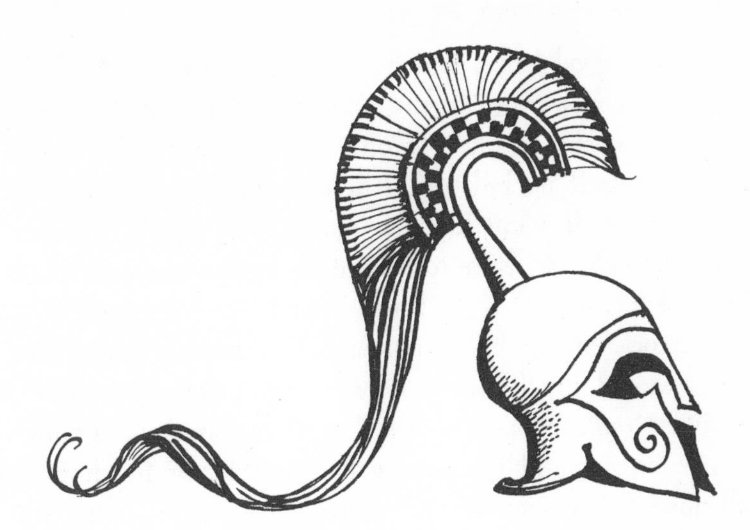

CHAPTER SIX

*

THE GREEKS WIN THE ADVANTAGE

The battle had not yet begun when Paris, dressed in a panther-skin cloak, darted between the two armies, carrying a sword, two spears, and a bow. He loudly challenged any Greek who dared to meet him in single combat. Bellowing for rage, Menelaus jumped from his chariot and ran at his mortal enemy. Since Menelaus wore full armour—helmet, breastplate, leg-guards, and all—Paris thought better of it and slipped back again into the Trojan ranks. His brother Hector cried in disgust: 'You cowardly, handsome, curly-headed, deceitful good-for-nothing! I wish you had never been born! The enemy are laughing at our disgrace. Upon my word, we must have been mad not to stone you long ago!'

Paris answered: 'You speak sensibly, brother; but why

blame my good looks, which the gods gave me at birth? It seems that you insist on my duelling with King Menelaus —very well, I'm ready! It's only fair for the two of us to fight it out. If he kills me, I don't grudge him Helen and her fortune. If I kill him, let her stay here. We can then return Apollo's treasure to his temple at Sparta, and all will be settled. But first I must arm myself like Menelaus.'

Hector, relieved by Paris's answer, strode along the Trojan line holding his spear at chest-level and pressing the soldiers back. 'Stop, and sit down!' he shouted. Though Greek arrows and slingstones flew at Hector in showers, all missed their aim; and when Agamemnon saw what was happening, he ordered: 'Leave Prince Hector alone, comrades! Probably he has something important to say.'

Hector turned around: 'Trojans and Greeks,' he announced, 'my brother, whose elopement with Queen Helen caused this miserable war, begs you to ground arms, and sit down. He and King Menelaus will presently fight to the death for this beautiful lady and her fortune. Meanwhile, we should agree on a truce.'

Menelaus accepted Paris's challenge; Agamemnon accepted the truce; and, after some delay due to the need for a sacrifice of lambs, both sides grounded arms, and the leaders dismounted from their chariots. Everyone welcomed the prospect of honourable peace.

Priam, his elder Councillors and Queen Helen, watching from the walls of Troy, saw Hector put two marked pebbles in his helmet and shake it to decide whether Paris or Menelaus should throw the first spear. Paris's pebble leaped out. When he had borrowed a splendid corslet from one of his brothers, a shield and helmet from a second, and a pair of leg-guards from a third, the champions advanced to meet each other, brandishing their weapons.

Paris's spear-throw struck Menelaus's shield fair and square; yet the point failed to pierce the thick layers of bull's hide under their bronze casing. Menelaus, in return, offered a prayer to Almighty Zeus and hurled his spear with terrific strength. It tore through Paris's shield, but he bent sideways and only his corslet was scratched. Menelaus then ran forward, sword in hand, and struck Paris's helmet so hard that the sword-blade snapped into four pieces. As Paris staggered, Menelaus caught hold of his horse-hair helmet crest and swung him bodily around. Half-strangled by the chin-strap, Paris found himself being dragged towards the Greek lines.

The duel would have ended in a glorious triumph for Menelaus, had not Aphrodite darted down to Paris's rescue. Reaching out an invisible hand, she broke the chin-strap and left Menelaus holding an empty helmet. He tossed this to his comrades, picked up Paris's spear, and turned to kill him. But Paris was no longer there! Aphrodite had made her favourite invisible and carried him to safety behind the lines.

When Paris could not be seen anywhere, Agamemnon shouted: 'Pray give me your attention, Trojans! I declare my brother Menelaus the winner! Now you must surrender Queen Helen and her fortune; and also pay me a huge indemnity to cover the costs of our expedition.'

His men yelled applause, and although the Trojans muttered curses against Paris, they could not dispute Menelaus's victory. Later, Helen, who had shut her eyes when Paris seemed on the point of being killed, heard from an old servant that he was back in their bedroom. She went to scold him for his cowardice, but he merely smiled and said: 'Athene helped Menelaus; Aphrodite helped me. What's more, she saved my life, as I knew she would. Well, Menelaus won that round; perhaps I'll win the next.'

Meanwhile, an argument took place in Heaven between Almighty Zeus and the other gods and goddesses. Zeus wanted to spare Troy, yet both Hera and Athene raised such protests that he let them have their way. Hera had even said: 'Destroy Argos, Mycenae, Sparta, or any other favourite city of mine; but I insist on the fall of Troy!' Athene saw that she could best keep the war alive (now that the Trojans were bound in honour to hand over Helen and her treasure) by making some Trojan ally break the truce. She therefore disguised herself as one of Priam's sons and told King Pandarus the Lycian: 'Take my advice, Pandarus, and shoot Menelaus while he is standing in the open. If you kill him, you'll earn undying glory, and Paris will give you a handsome reward as well.'

Pandarus unwisely followed Athene's advice. He reached for his bow, made from a pair of four-foot oryx-horns clamped together at their bases; strung it, fitted an arrow to the string, and let fly. Athene naturally had no intention of allowing her friend Menelaus to be killed. She stood in front of him and guided the arrow where it would do the least damage. The point just nicked his side and drew a little blood. But the truce had been broken.

Some minutes later the two armies met head on, with a clatter of shields and a clash of weapons. Hundreds of dead soon strewed the plain. The fight surged this way and that, until at last Hector's Trojans fell back, and the Greeks began greedily stripping enemy corpses of their arms and armour.

Diomedes, King of Argos, fought best that day, though Agamemnon, Menelaus, Great Ajax, and other Greek leaders also accounted for a large number of the enemy. Athene herself helped Diomedes, as he stormed across the battle-field in his chariot, spearing men by the score, and seldom troubling to strip their corpses. Pandarus halted him awhile with an arrow that pierced his shoulderplate; but when it had been pulled out by his charioteer, Athene gave him renewed strength to kill many more of the enemy.

Aeneas then invited Pandarus to mount his chariot, drawn by two mares of divine breed, faster than the wind. 'I'll drive, you fight,' he suggested. 'Together we should easily destroy this Argive champion.'

Pandarus mounted. 'I thought,' he said, 'that my arrow had gone home; but Diomedes seems to be protected by some god or goddess. This time I'll use my spear and make sure of him.'

Diomedes saw them approaching at a gallop. He told his charioteer: 'Don't be afraid! We're protected by Athene. As soon as I've killed those two kings, abandon our chariot, seize Prince Aeneas's, and drive it to the camp. His mares are of a divine breed, worth twenty of mine.'

Pandarus flung the first spear. It tore through Diomedes's shield, dinting his breastplate, but went no farther. Diomedes's spear, guided by Athene, struck Pandarus between the eyes and killed him outright. Aeneas dismounted to stand guard over the fallen body. Diomedes dismounted too; he picked up and flung an enormous rock which broke Aeneas's thigh-bone. When Aphrodite flew down and wrapped him in a fold of her white robe, Diomedes at once knew who she was. He daringly lunged with his spear, and wounded her palm just above the wrist. Gods and goddesses never bleed—but a colourless liquid, called 'ichor', oozed from the spear-jab. Aphrodite dropped Aeneas, screamed, fled to the War-god Ares, who sat watching the battle from a hill near by, and collapsed in his chariot. Iris, the Messenger of the Gods, kindly drove her back, sobbing for pain, to Olympus.

Diomedes, meanwhile, would have finished off Aeneas —whose chariot was already on its way to the naval camp— if Apollo had not flourished a sword, shouting in terrible tones: 'Beware, rash mortal! You dared attack the Goddess Aphrodite, but this is the God Apollo!'

Hector, helped by Ares, who was siding with the Trojans, then led a bold counter-attack. Aeneas, whom Apollo had taken to his neighbouring temple and instantly healed, ran up to support him, and together they killed whole companies of Greeks.

CHAPTER SEVEN

*

THE TROJANS WIN THE ADVANTAGE

With Almighty Zeus's permission, Athene mounted her divine chariot and went in search of Diomedes. She found him pale-faced and quiet, still losing blood from the arrow wound. 'Come aboard and fight Ares!' she commanded, giving him renewed strength. Diomedes obeyed, and together they galloped off. Athene made herself invisible, and when Ares stabbed murderously at Diomedes, she drew the spear aside, while Diomedes lunged at his stomach. As the blade sank in, Ares bellowed louder than nine or ten thousand men, then fled to Olympus, where he showed Zeus the ichor welling in streams from his wound. 'How dare mortals treat gods so impiously?' he complained.

Zeus called him a stubborn, violent fool, even worse than

his mother Hera; but let Apollo heal him. To be fair, he stopped Athene fighting, too.

Diomedes came face to face with a Lycian named Glaucus and, after challenging him, discovered that his own grandfather Oeneus the Argonaut—who planted the first vineyard in Greece—had been a close friend of Glaucus's grandfather Bellerophon who killed the monstrous Chimaera. Because of this family tie, they decided not to fight it out, and Diomedes said: 'Let us exchange arms, in open acknowledgement of our friendship!' Glaucus, realizing that he stood no chance against so powerful a champion, agreed to the exchange; although he wore golden armour, and Diomedes only bronze.

Hector paid a hurried visit to Troy. Scores of women crowded around him, begging news of their sons or husbands; but he pushed them aside, and went to find his mother, Queen Hecuba. 'Unless you make these women offer public prayers and sacrifices,' he said, 'we're lost. It's Athene, above all, whom you must honour. She's been unusually hard on us today.' He then visited Paris's house, and found him burnishing his breastplate with a soft leather cloth. 'You cowardly rascal!' he cried. 'How dare you stay away from a battle in which so many brave Trojans are dying for your sake?'

Paris answered: 'You speak sensibly, brother; but the truth is that, feeling a little sad after fighting Menelaus, I came home for a good cry on this chair. Dear Helen has just suggested that I should go out again, and I'm getting my armour ready. One never knows who'll win the next round, does one?'

Helen begged Hector to forgive her. 'All the disasters I've brought on Troy aren't really my fault,' she sobbed.

'The gods arranged everything. I couldn't disobey Aphrodite. Please sit down and rest awhile. You look so tired.'

Hector would not wait. He hurried away and met his wife Andromache in the street, carrying Scamandrius, their three-year-old son. Andromache tried to hold him back. 'Stay here, in safety,' she pleaded. 'Don't make me a widow, don't orphan our darling boy!' He answered: 'Honour forbids me to avoid battle, even though I know that my family and friends are doomed. Worst of all, I confess, is the thought that you'll be led weeping into slavery by some cruel Greek prince–forced to drudge as a servant, and to be rudely stared at when people say: "Look, that's Andromache–she was once Hector the Trojan's wife!"' Scamandrius began to cry, scared by Andromache's tears and by his father's tall plume; so Hector took the helmet off and dandled him in his arms, begging Andromache to control herself and not make things more difficult still. 'War is a man's task: leave me to it! If I must die, I must die.'

They parted. Paris then ran up, fully armed, apologizing for being late, and the brothers went into battle side by side.

Hector loudly challenged any Greek prince to meet him in a duel. Nobody dared accept, until King Menelaus stepped forward. He was groaning quietly to himself, well aware what little hope he had of defeating Hector; so the other Councillors restrained him, and nine of them even offered to take his place. Among these were Agamemnon, Diomedes, Great Ajax, Little Ajax, Idomeneus of Crete, and Odysseus. They marked nine pebbles and put them into a helmet, which Old Nestor shook. Great Ajax's pebble jumped out, to his joy, and a terrific fight between him and Hector now took place. Ajax carried a huge tall shield–nine layers of bull's hide sheathed in bronze; Hector pre-

ferred a small round targe. When each had made a spear-cast and failed to score a hit, they began hurling enormous boulders. Though Ajax knocked Hector down with one as big as a mill-stone, he rose again and drew his sword. Ajax drew his. But before they could hack at each other, heralds ran up from the Greek side as well as the Trojan, and used their sacred wands to part the two champions. 'Stop fighting!' they cried. 'Respect the Goddess of Night, who is about to drop her curtain on your encounter.' Both politely agreed, and Hector proposed that after so noble a duel they ought to exchange gifts of friendly admiration.

'Nothing would please me better,' answered Ajax. He gave Hector an embroidered purple belt, and in return got a silver-studded sword. (With this belt Hector was later dragged to death; and with this sword Ajax later killed himself.) The armies thereupon marched back to their suppers.

Antenor spoke at King Priam's Council meeting. He pointed out that Paris, having violated the laws of hospitality by stealing Helen, had made things even worse by running away from Menelaus in the duel. 'We swore an oath to Zeus that the winner should have Helen; she must therefore be sent home with all her treasure.'

Paris rose. 'I refuse to surrender Helen,' he cried, 'because I didn't steal her. She came here of her own free will. However, the booty I captured at Sidon has enriched me, and I'm ready to pay Menelaus full compensation.'

Priam thanked Paris for so noble a statement. Meanwhile he suggested a twenty-four-hour truce, during which both sides might bury their dead. The Greeks, though rejecting Paris's offer, welcomed the truce and, working like ants all the next day, raised a barrow of earth over their dead. They set it as a rampart alongside the camp, and fortified it with a turreted stone wall. The removal of so much earth formed a deep ditch, or fosse, in front.

Their one mistake was not to offer the huge sacrifice that Almighty Zeus expected on such occasions; and when dawn ended the truce, he showed his annoyance by granting the Trojans a favourable sign—thunder on their right hand, from Mount Ida—which at the same time scared the Greeks. Odysseus deserted King Nestor who, although too old to fight, had been busily riding about the battlefield in his chariot, encouraging the troops. Diomedes saved him from capture; but when a thunderbolt thrown by Zeus struck the ground close to his horses' hooves, even he retreated.

Hector's Trojans rushed forward, spearing the frightened Greeks as they ran, and had soon driven the survivors behind their rampart. Another few minutes, and they would have burned the fleet; however, Agamemnon made a pitiful prayer to Zeus, who relented and inspired Diomedes to lead a chariot sortie.

The most successful Greek fighter that morning was Great Ajax's half-brother Teucer the Archer, Hesione's son. Using Ajax's tall shield as cover, he would peep around the rim, take quick aim at a Trojan, shoot, and hide again. He had killed nine men before Hector broke his collarbone with a well-flung rock. Once more the Greeks turned tail and fled, pursued by the triumphant Hector, who slaughtered them until nightfall.

In Heaven, Hera raged like a Fury. 'Show a little patience,' Athene said. 'Wait a little longer for my Father to fulfil the promise he gave Thetis. He has sworn to make Agamemnon beg Achilles's pardon and offer him vast treasures, if only he stops sulking in his hut and fights again.' Nevertheless, Hera forced Athene to step into her golden chariot. 'Together, my girl, we'll turn the tide of battle,' she announced grimly.

Zeus, who was watching from Mount Ida, sent them a message by Iris: 'If you don't get out of that chariot at once, I'll hurl my thunderbolt at it!' They obeyed, and presently Zeus told Hera: 'Very well, wife—just to punish you for meddling, I'll let the Trojans win an even bigger victory tomorrow!'

That night the Trojans camped close to the enemy rampart, confident of success. The Greeks were so disheartened by their losses that when, at a Council meeting, Agamemnon wanted to raise the siege and sail home, Diomedes alone dared say: 'That would be the act of a coward. I'm going to stay and fight to the last, even if you all leave me!'

Old Nestor supported Diomedes, adding: 'My lords, our one hope of survival now lies in calming Achilles and persuading him to take the field.' And Agamemnon, since Nestor had not said anything disrespectful, readily admitted his past folly, at the same time promising to apologize and give Achilles a huge compensation for the insult—seven three-legged bronze kettles, ten gold ingots weighing over eighty pounds apiece, twenty polished copper cauldrons, six pairs of prize-winning chariot-horses, seven beautiful girl captives who embroidered marvellously—and to send back Briseis. 'Also, once I'm home in Greece,' he said, 'I'll award Achilles the same rank and honours as my own son Orestes, and one of my three daughters for a wife, whichever he prefers, and seven cities to rule.'

Nestor thanked Agamemnon on behalf of the Council. He suggested that Great Ajax and Odysseus should take the offer to Achilles, accompanied by his old tutor Phoenix. Yet when they arrived, Achilles refused to accept any gift from Agamemnon. 'That rascal behaved,' said he, 'with unpardonable meanness. I can never forget how he robbed me of Briseis, whom I was going to marry.' Though treating his three visitors courteously, he told them straight out: 'I shall sail for Greece tomorrow, and leave Agamemnon to his fate.' Phoenix called him stubborn and stony-hearted. Since, however, nothing more could be done, he wiped away his tears and decided to go too.

CHAPTER EIGHT

*

THE CAMP ENDANGERED

That night, Agamemnon could not sleep. He got up, armed himself, and went in search of his brother Menelaus. 'What we need,' he told Menelaus, 'is a really clever scheme for saving our army and fleet. Wake Great Ajax and King Idomeneus of Crete! Something may occur to them.' Everyone felt vexed at being dragged out of bed in the pitch dark, after a hard day's fighting. Yet Agamemnon called so loudly for immediate action that the Council decided to send scouts into the no-man's-land between the camp and the Trojan lines, hoping vaguely that they might bring back news of Hector's plans.

Diomedes volunteered, and when asked to pick a companion, chose Odysseus. Odysseus agreed to come, remembering that Diomedes had seen him shamefully desert Nestor in battle a few hours before. He wanted to clear his good name.

The two set out together across the fosse, and soon stumbled in the dark over a Trojan scout named Dolon. Having made him give them as much useful information as he could, they mercilessly cut his throat. Odysseus hid Dolon's ferret-skin cap, wolf-skin cloak, bow and spear, in a tamarisk bush; then hurried with Diomedes towards the Trojan right flank where, Dolon had told them, they would find King Rhesus of Thrace encamped. No sentries were on duty, so they crawled up stealthily, murdered Rhesus and twelve officers lying asleep beside him, and then drove off his magnificent horses: white as snow and swifter than the wind. They also recovered Dolon's spoils on the way home. Rhesus had arrived at Troy this same evening; and the capture of his team was a remarkable piece of luck for Diomedes and Odysseus, because a prophecy that the Greeks could never capture Troy once these horses had drunk Scamander water, still remained to be fulfilled.

The following day Almighty Zeus again favoured Troy, though King Agamemnon enjoyed a short spell of glory. He headed a chariot charge, speared several Trojan noblemen, and was already close to the City walls when Zeus decided to change the fortunes of battle.

He sent Hector an order to rally and encourage his forces, yet to attempt nothing for the next half-hour; as soon as Agamemnon left the field, the Trojans might slaughter the leaderless Greeks without pause all afternoon. Presently, Agamemnon killed Antenor's two sons; but one of them, before dying, speared him through the arm, just above the elbow. Agamemnon went on fighting, until his wound grew so painful that he turned his chariot about and drove off, weeping miserably.

Hector at once led a strong attack and, though stunned for awhile when Diomedes flung a spear that struck the crest-socket of his helmet, began pressing the Greeks backward. Paris, hidden behind a stone pillar which marked the tomb of his grandfather, then took aim at Diomedes's foot and pinned it to the ground with an arrow.

Diomedes called Paris a nasty-mouthed, mean, jealous trouble-maker, proud of his toy bow and kiss-curl. 'If we met, spear against spear, what would your chances of victory be?' he bellowed. Nevertheless, after extracting the arrow, he felt so sick that he, too, left the field, and Odysseus had to battle for his life against swarms of Trojans. Hector drove along the bank of the river Scamander, where the Thessalians offered him stiff resistance, until Paris lodged an arrow in the shoulder of their King Machaon, who was not only the best surgeon in Greece but one of the boldest chariot fighters. Nestor rescued Machaon and drove him safely to camp; after which Great Ajax's steadfastness alone saved the Greek army from complete rout.

Achilles, as he stood on the stern of his beached ship and watched the distant battle, saw Nestor returning at a gallop. His friend Patroclus, whom he sent to ask the wounded king's name, found Nestor already in his hut. A slave-girl was pouring out for Machaon a cool drink of barley boiled in onion juice and sweetened with honey. They invited Patroclus to join them, which he did. After bemoaning the Greek losses, Nestor remarked: 'It seems that Achilles will not fight because of some divine message or other; but surely he cannot wish to see us massacred? Perhaps, if you asked him tactfully, he might let you lead his famous Myrmidons against Hector? They are fine troops, fresh and well-trained, and their appearance on the field might turn the tide of battle in our favour.'

Hector's forces were now ready to storm the Greek rampart and burn the fleet. They swarmed over the fosse, scaled the parapet, and had soon captured a wide length of wall, despite the stubborn defence by Great Ajax, also by Teucer the Archer, whose broken collarbone had miraculously healed, and their cousin Little Ajax, who always fought without armour—his javelins seldom missed their aim.

Almighty Zeus granted Hector the supreme honour of first entering the Greek camp. He seized a huge boulder and ran towards the main entrance. The high, massive gates were strengthened with cross-bars bolted together. Planting himself a short distance away and advancing one foot, he aimed at the very centre of the gates and let fly. They burst open and Hector rushed through, the light of victory in his eyes, followed by a column of exulting Trojans. The Greeks fled panic-stricken to their ships.

Poseidon, enraged at Hector's success, hurried down from Olympus to his undersea palace off the island of Euboea, where he harnessed a chariot drawn by sea-beasts, put on a golden corslet, grasped an elegant gold whip, and drove across the waves to Troy. There he stabled his team in a sea-cave between the islands of Imbros and Tenedos, and entered the camp on foot, disguised as Calchas. Poseidon dared not take an open part in the war for fear of vexing his brother, Almighty Zeus; nevertheless, he encouraged the Greeks, and with two taps of his staff gave Great Ajax, Little Ajax and Teucer such battle-fury that their hands and feet seemed to weigh nothing. However, Hector and Paris kept up the Trojan attack; and the fight roared on.

Hera now borrowed from Aphrodite the world-famous girdle which forced whomever the wearer pleased to fall madly in love with her. 'I need it,' Hera lied smoothly, 'for an aged aunt of mine, a Sea-goddess whose husband

grew tired of her centuries ago. I should be glad to renew their love. They live a most miserable life on the sea-bottom, always snapping at each other because of some stale old quarrel.'

Hera really wanted to use the girdle herself. When she buckled it on, her husband, Almighty Zeus, to whom she had lately seemed the ugliest and stupidest of all goddesses, felt such passionate love for her that he lost interest in the war. Hera fondled him affectionately and lay down beside him in a valley on Mount Ida, where the earth at once sprouted grass, clover, crocuses and hyacinth flowers around them.

Afterwards she persuaded the God of Sleep to close his eyes, and as soon as he began to snore, sent a message to Poseidon: 'Do what you please—the coast is clear!' Poseidon now boldly led the Greek attack. Diomedes and Odysseus followed just behind. Hector and Great Ajax again met face to face. Ajax threw a rock which flew over the rim of Hector's shield, catching him below the neck. He spun around like a top, and was carried off the field, moaning and vomiting blood. The Trojans fled.

When Zeus awoke and saw Poseidon pursuing a mob of Trojan fugitives, he threatened to punish Hera as she deserved. Hera, however, still wearing Aphrodite's girdle, could afford to laugh at his threats, and deny that she had encouraged Poseidon's appearance on the battlefield. So Zeus merely warned him, through Iris: 'Break off the fight at once, brother, or suffer the consequences!'

Poseidon's answer was so rude that she tactfully waited in silence until he thought better of it, and after awhile, indeed, he sulkily obeyed orders. Thereupon Zeus lent his magic shield to Apollo, who shook it in the Greeks' faces, scaring them to a halt, then flew to Hector's side and instantly cured him. The Greeks lost courage and, a few minutes later the Trojans, led by Hector and Aeneas, were slaughtering them by the hundred. They quickly forced their way into the camp, and this time reached the ships which, it will be recalled, were drawn up in rows, with a line of huts separating each of these. All the Greeks except Great Ajax abandoned the first row. He stood aboard the ship that had once belonged to Protesilaus, grasping a thirty-foot pike of the kind wielded in sea-battles by no less than five sailors, and spitted on it dozens of Trojans who brought torches, trying to burn him out.

CHAPTER NINE

*

ACHILLES AVENGES PATROCLUS

Patroclus begged Achilles to lend him his own suit of armour and the command of his warlike Myrmidons. 'With their help,' he pleaded, 'I can drive away the Trojans before the fleet is burned and our surviving friends are massacred.' Achilles consented, but made Patroclus promise that once the camp had been cleared of enemies, he would not try to win further glory by chasing them back and attacking Troy itself.

Great Ajax could no longer defend his ship, because Hector lopped off the pike-head and left him only the pole. He jumped down and rejoined his comrades, who were holding the nearest row of huts. This allowed the Trojans to set the ship on fire. As soon as Achilles saw a thin column of smoke rising into the sky, he lent Patroclus his magnificent arms and armour, paraded the Myrmidons, and sent them forward to save the fleet. Their charge was irresistible. Mistaking Patroclus for Achilles, the Trojans were again driven out, and lost heavily.

Almighty Zeus, watching from Mount Ida, could not at first decide whether Patroclus should be immediately destroyed by Hector and stripped of Achilles's armour, or whether he should be granted fresh victories. In the end, Zeus let him go on for another half hour. Patroclus forgot his promise to Achilles as he chased the fleeing Trojans across the plain. A company of Myrmidons were already scaling the walls of Troy—the weak part built by Aeacus—when Apollo showed himself on the Citadel and shook his terrible shield at them. They retired in awe.

Hector then challenged Patroclus to a duel. No sooner had they dismounted from their chariots than Apollo stepped quietly behind Patroclus and struck him on the neck with the edge of his palm. Achilles's helmet tumbled off, Achilles's tough spear shattered, Achilles's shield slipped to the ground, and Patroclus stood there unarmed, dazed and trembling. Darting up, Hector speared him low in the belly; and the Trojans rallied when they saw his fall.

A fearful tussle followed for the body. Both Greeks and Trojans treated it like a newly-flayed bull's hide, which farm-boys tug in all directions, to stretch and supple it. At last Menelaus and Idomeneus's lieutenant, Meriones the Cretan, succeeded in carrying the body back to camp, while Great and Little Ajax acted as rear-guards.

One of Nestor's sons brought the bad news to Achilles, tears blinding his eyes. Achilles's two horses, Xanthus and Balius, which Patroclus had been driving, wept too—huge tears trickled down their noses. But he already knew. Hera had sent a message by Iris, and ordered him to stand on the rampart as soon as the Trojans appeared, and roar out a challenge. This would make them recoil in terror because, having watched Hector strip his well-known armour from Patroclus, they thought him dead. Achilles shouted so loud, and the Greeks halted in such confusion, that forty of them were wounded by the spears of men following behind, or run over by chariots.

Achilles wept, laid his enormous hands on Patroclus's bloody chest, howling horribly, like a lioness whose cub has been killed, and mourned all night long.

Thetis then persuaded Hephaestus, the lame Smith-god, to forge her son a new set of divine arms and armour. Hephaestus began his work immediately: ornamenting the shield with town and country scenes designed in silver, gold and precious stones. At dawn, Thetis brought her splendid gift to Achilles's hut. He put it on delightedly and was soon making a speech at a General Assembly.

'King Agamemnon,' he said, 'neither of us has profited in the least from our recent unfortunate quarrel about my slave-girl. The results have been so bad for you and me that I almost wish she'd never been captured alive. Come, let bygones be bygones! And since your wounded arm still keeps you out of battle, why not make me temporary Commander-in-Chief?'

Agamemnon agreed. He even admitted his unfair treatment of Achilles, though blaming it on the Fates and a dark Fury called Mischief who, together, had robbed him of his senses.

When Achilles asked permission to advance at once, Agamemnon answered: 'I fear I can't grant you that favour. The men haven't yet breakfasted. But while their food is being got ready, I'll send servants to my store-hut, and have all the treasures fetched that I recently offered you.'

'I want no treasures,' shouted Achilles, 'and the mere thought of breakfast nauseates me, with so many dead strewing the field!'

Nevertheless, Agamemnon's servants brought him the gold ingots, the tripods, the cauldrons, the slave-girls—including Briseis—and the race-horses. Briseis flung herself on Patroclus's corpse, wailing loudly and praising his gentle, generous nature. 'He had always promised,' she sobbed, 'that Prince Achilles and I would be married in Greece, as soon as Troy fell.' Achilles, it seems, had kept his love of Polyxena a secret even from Patroclus.

He still refused to eat, but Athene gave him divine nourishment by smearing nectar and ambrosia on his skin, which made him feel enormously strong. Both armies then poured into the plain, where Almighty Zeus varied the day's battle by letting all the gods and goddesses take part, and fight one another if they pleased. There were five on each side. For the Greeks: Hera, Athene, Poseidon, Hermes the Herald, and Hephaestus the Smith. For the Trojans: Ares the War-god, Apollo, his sister Artemis the Huntress, his mother the Goddess Leto, and the River-god Scamander.

When the lines of battle clashed, Apollo kept Achilles from meeting Hector. He went to Aeneas in disguise and reminded him of his drunken boast at a recent banquet: 'I'm ready to challenge the bravest of the Greeks—even Prince Achilles!'

Aeneas answered: 'That's very true. The last time we met I was unarmed, and a neutral—I had to run for my life. Besides, Athene was helping him, and no wise man opposes the gods.'

Apollo inspired him with courage. 'You also are under divine protection, Aeneas,' he said, 'and far better born than Achilles. His mother Thetis is an unimportant Sea-goddess;

your mother is Aphrodite, a respected member of Zeus's Olympian Council.'

So Aeneas challenged Achilles, who only jeered at him, asking: 'Are you out to win King Priam's favour and get named as his successor? Why fool yourself?' When Aeneas did not reply, he went on: 'Priam still has several sons of his own. He'd never prefer a cousin to a son. Take my advice: retire unhurt!' 'And you, I suppose, fancy yourself as Agamemnon's successor?' Aeneas shouted, stung to anger.

Achilles found equally unkind things to say in return, but at last Aeneas, somehow controlling his temper, said: 'Why are we standing about and arguing like little boys? Words are cheap, so are insults. If we had time to spare, we could exchange enough of them to fill a two-hundred-oar galley. I came here to fight, not to gossip. Guard your head!'

The spear, flung with all his strength, made no dint in the wonderful shield that Hephaestus had forged; whereas Achilles's spear drove clean through the top of Aeneas's targe, burying itself in the ground behind him. Aeneas picked up a huge rock which, if he had thrown it, must merely have bounced back from the divine armour. Yet Poseidon knew that Almighty Zeus would be enraged if Aeneas, whose life he had decided to spare for his own best reasons, were to die. So he shrouded Achilles's eyes in a magical mist, and swung Aeneas high above the battlefield; laying him down beyond the Trojan lines, where his arrival greatly surprised some allied troops who were late in arming themselves. Achilles, no less surprised to find him vanished, shrugged his shoulders and went in search of Hector. He caught sight of twelve-year-old Polydorus, King Priam's youngest and favourite son. The boy, despite strict orders to avoid danger, was dodging between the front row of fighters. Achilles transfixed his body with a javelin.

Though Hector had been warned by Apollo to avoid Achilles's rage, the death of his little brother so infuriated him that he ran up, vengefully shaking a long spear.

'We meet at last!' cried Achilles.

Hector threw the spear, but a gust of wind sent by Athene made it curve back and fall at his feet. When Achilles rushed forward yelling vengeance, Apollo shrouded Hector in another thick mist. Three times Achilles vainly charged at his invisible enemy, then turned his anger against lesser Trojans, roaring on like a forest fire as they broke and fled towards the Scamander. There, in the shallows and in hollows under the river banks, he massacred hundreds of them. The angry River-god Scamander appeared in human shape, crying 'Begone!' Achilles furiously sprang into mid-stream and yelled a challenge. Scamander gathered a great head of water and brought it rushing at Achilles, who braced himself by clutching at an elm-tree. This was soon uprooted, but he scrambled ashore, chased by Scamander in the form of a towering green wave. He would have drowned like a rat, had not Poseidon and Athene dragged him away, each holding a hand.

Scamander and his partner, the River-god Simoeis, together pursued Achilles as he hurried off, but Hera ordered her son Hephaestus to oppose them. He kindled a fierce blaze on the plain, which burned the elms, willows, tamarisks, rushes and sedge of the river bank. Scamander's water soon boiled with such furious heat, that he appealed to Hera in pain and terror. 'Please recall your son!' he pleaded. 'I'll promise never to help Troy again.' Hera did as he asked, and Achilles continued his slaughter of Trojans.

Some other gods and goddesses had already come to blows. Ares attacked Athene, but his spear proved useless against the shield lent her by Almighty Zeus, and, throwing a huge black boundary-stone at his head, she knocked him flat. Ares's fallen body covered seven acres of land. Aphrodite was helping him to his feet, when Athene, at Hera's orders, felled her with a tremendous slap on the chest.

Hermes would not fight against the Goddess Leto, mother of Apollo and Artemis. He replied politely to her invitation: 'Madam, the victory is already yours.' Poseidon then challenged Apollo to a single combat, which he also refused. 'Why should we Gods injure each other for the sake of a few wretched mortals?' he asked calmly. Artemis the Huntress screamed at her brother, calling him a pitiful coward, but Hera rushed up, seized both of Artemis's wrists in one hand, snatched bow and arrows from her, and soundly boxed her ears.

Achilles meanwhile drove the Trojans headlong towards Troy, where Priam opened all the gates to admit them. Hector alone stood fast, in defence of the Western gateway. Priam wept and tore his white hair, begging him to come inside quickly, before he was shut out. Hector would not listen and, as Achilles rushed to the attack, turned and ran at great speed around the walls, hoping that the Trojans would drop heavy stones on his pursuer from the battlements. Achilles, however, followed too close behind to make this possible. The pair circled Troy four times. At last Athene, disguised as Hector's brother Prince Deiphobus, appeared beside him, yelling: 'Stop, Hector! Let us meet Achilles together, two against one!'

Deceived by the Goddess, he halted, faced about, and said sadly: 'Achilles, since this is a death-duel, you and I should swear that whoever kills and strips the other, will send the corpse to his people for decent burial.'

Achilles's only reply was the whiz of a spear. Hector ducked, and hurled his own, which bounced harmlessly from the divine shield. He called over his shoulder: 'Quick, Deiphobus, lend me yours!' Getting no answer, Hector realized that Athene was tricking him. He drew his broadsword and charged. Athene had meanwhile invisibly restored Achilles's spear to him. Taking aim at Hector's bare neck, he sent his enemy crashing down.

'Spare my corpse,' Hector whispered. 'King Priam will ransom it at a noble price.' 'Scoundrel!' shouted Achilles. 'For the injury you've done me, I'll let the crows pick out your eyes and the dogs crunch your bones.'

So Hector died. Achilles stripped his body naked, then cut slits behind his heel-tendons, pulled Ajax's embroidered belt through them, buckled it to the tailboard of his chariot, lashed the team on, and dragged Hector after him, round and round the walls of Troy. Priam, Hecuba and Andromache all watched horror-stricken from above.

Back in the camp, Achilles built a hundred-foot-square pyre for Patroclus's corpse, and there sacrificed a huge flock of sheep to his ghost; also four horses, nine hounds, and twelve noble Trojan prisoners of war, whom he had reserved for this fate. The blaze lit up many miles of the countryside. Next day he held funeral games in Patroclus's honour: a chariot race, a boxing bout, a wrestling match, a foot race and a javelin-throwing competition, all with valuable prizes. Still crazed by grief, he would rise every dawn to drag Hector's corpse three times round Patroclus's tomb. Apollo, however, tenderly protected it from decay or mutilation.

At last the God Hermes led King Priam to Achilles's hut under cover of darkness, and commanded Achilles to accept a fair ransom: the corpse's weight in pure gold. Priam loathed having to clasp his enemy's knees and kiss the terrible hands that had murdered so many of his sons, but

forced himself to undergo this shame. Achilles treated him courteously, and even praised his courage in entering the enemy camp at night. They agreed on the ransom. However, by now so little gold remained in Priam's treasury, that when they presently met in the temple of Apollo, his daughter Polyxena had to tip down the scale with her necklace and bracelets.

Achilles, impressed by this sisterly kindness and still deeply in love, told Priam: 'I'll cheerfully exchange your dead son for your living daughter. Keep this gold, marry her to me, and if you then return Helen to Menelaus, I'll arrange an honourable peace between our two peoples.'

Priam answered: 'No, take the gold, as we agreed, and let me have my son's body. But I'm ready to barter one live woman against another. Persuade your comrades to leave Helen at Troy, and I'll ask no marriage fee for Polyxena. We should be lost without Helen.'

Achilles undertook to do his best.

CHAPTER TEN

*

THE WOODEN HORSE

The war dragged on. New allies came to King Priam's help, including the Amazon Queen Penthesileia from Armenia, who killed King Machaon and three times drove Achilles himself off the field. Finally, with Athene's help, Achilles ran her through. Memnon, the negro King of Ethiopia, accounted for hundreds of Greeks, including Nestor's eldest son, and almost succeeded in burning the Greek ships; but Great Ajax challenged him to a duel, which was rudely interrupted by Achilles. He ran up, brushed Ajax aside, speared Memnon, and threw the Trojans back once more.

This proved to be Achilles's last victory, because when that night he met Polyxena by private arrangement in Apollo's temple, she wormed out of him his most important secret. Polyxena was sworn to avenge her beloved brother

Hector, and there is nothing a beautiful girl cannot make a man tell her as a proof of love. He revealed that when Thetis dipped him in Styx water as a child, to make him invulnerable, she had tightly held his right heel, which stayed dry and unprotected.

They met again next day at the same place, to confirm his promise that, after marrying Polyxena, he would so arrange matters that the Greeks went home without Helen. King Priam had insisted on his offering a sacrifice to Apollo and taking an oath at the God's altar. Achilles came barefoot and unarmed; but two of Priam's sons, whom he sent to represent him, were secretly plotting murder. Prince Deiphobus embraced Achilles, in pretence of friendship, while Paris, hiding behind a pillar, shot at his heel. The barbed arrow, guided by Aphrodite, wounded him mortally. Though Achilles snatched firebrands from the altar and struck vengefully at Paris and Deiphobus, they got away; and he killed a couple of temple servants only.

Odysseus and Great Ajax, who suspected Achilles of treachery, had crept after him into the temple. Dying in their arms, he made them swear that when Troy fell they would sacrifice Polyxena at his tomb. Paris and Deiphobus returned to fetch the body; but Odysseus and Ajax beat them off in a stiff fight and brought it safely back.

Agamemnon, Menelaus and the rest of the Council shed tears at Achilles's funeral, though few ordinary soldiers regretted the death of so notorious a traitor. His ashes, mixed with those of Patroclus, were placed in a golden urn and buried in a lofty barrow at the entrance to the Hellespont.

Thetis awarded Achilles's arms and armour to the bravest Greek leader left before Troy; and to embarrass Agamemnon, for whom she felt a deep scorn, appointed him the judge. Odysseus and Great Ajax, having successfully defended his corpse against the Trojans, came forward as rivals for this honour. But Agamemnon feared the anger of whoever lost so valuable a prize, and sent spies by night to listen under the walls of Troy and report what the Trojans themselves thought.

The spies crept up close, and after awhile a party of Trojan girls began to chat above them. One praised Ajax's courage in lifting Achilles's corpse on his shoulders and taking it through a shower of spears and arrows. Another said: 'Nonsense, Odysseus showed far greater courage! Even a slave-girl will do what Ajax did, if given a corpse to carry; but put weapons in her hand, and she'll never dare use them. Ajax used that corpse as a shield, while Odysseus kept our men off with spear and sword.'

On the strength of this report, Agamemnon awarded the arms to Odysseus. The Council knew that he would never have preferred him to Great Ajax if Achilles had been alive —Achilles thought the world of his gallant cousin. Besides, the spies understood no Phrygian, and were probably prompted by Odysseus. Yet no one dared say so.

In a blind rage, Ajax swore revenge on Agamemnon, Menelaus, Odysseus, and their fellow-Councillors. That night Athene sent him mad and he ran howling, sword in hand, among the flocks he had captured in raids on Trojan farms. After immense butchery, he chained the surviving sheep and goats together, hauled them to camp, and went on with his bloody work. He chose two rams, cut out the tongue of the largest, which he mistook for Agamemnon, and lopped off its head. Then he tied the other to a pillar by the neck and flogged it unmercifully, screaming abuse and shouting: 'Take that, and that, and that, treacherous Odysseus!' At last, coming to his senses, and greatly ashamed of himself, he fixed the sword which Hector had given him upright in the ground, and leaped upon it. His last words were a prayer to the Furies for vengeance. Odysseus wisely avoided this danger by presenting the armour to Achilles's ten-year-old son Neoptolemus, who had just joined the Greek forces and, like his father at the same age, was already full-grown. His mother had been one of the princesses among whom Thetis hid Achilles at Scyros.

Calchas prophesied that Troy could be taken only with the help of Heracles's bow and arrows, now owned by King Philoctetes. Odysseus and Diomedes sailed to fetch them from the small island off Lemnos where Philoctetes was still marooned. Even after nine years, his wound smelt as badly as ever, nor had the pain grown less. Odysseus stole his bow and arrows by a trick; but Diomedes, not wishing to be mixed up in so dishonourable an affair, made him restore them, and persuaded Philoctetes to come aboard their ship. When they landed at Troy, Machaon's brother cured him with soothing herbs and a precious stone called serpentine.

No sooner was Philoctetes well again than he challenged Paris to an archery duel. Paris shot first, and aimed at his enemy's heart, but the arrow went wide—Athene, of course, saw to that. Philoctetes then let loose three arrows in quick succession. The first pierced Paris's bow-hand, the next his right eye, and the last his ankle. He hobbled from the fight and, though Menelaus tried to catch and kill him, managed to reach Troy and die in Helen's arms.

Helen was now a widow, but King Priam could still not bear the idea of restoring her to Menelaus; and his sons wrangled among themselves, each wanting to be her husband. Helen then remembered that she had been Queen of Sparta and Menelaus's wife. One night a sentry caught her as she was about to climb down a rope from the battlements; whereupon Deiphobus married her by force—an act which disgusted the entire royal family.

Jealous quarrels between Priam's sons grew so fierce that he sent Antenor to discuss peace terms with the Greeks. But Antenor had not forgiven Deiphobus for having helped Paris to murder Achilles in Apollo's own temple, a sacrilege which Priam left unpunished. He told Agamemnon's Council that he would betray Troy if they made him King afterwards and gave him half the spoils. According to an ancient oracle, he said, Troy would not fall until the Palladium, a legless wooden image of Athene, some four feet high, had been stolen from her temple on the Citadel. As it happened, the Greeks already knew of this prophecy through Helenus, who was madly jealous of Deiphobus's marriage. So Antenor promised to hand over the Palladium when Athene's two favourites, Odysseus and Diomedes, had entered Troy by a secret way he would show them.

That night, Odysseus and Diomedes set out together and, following Antenor's instructions, cleared away a pile of stones under the western wall. They found that it hid the exit of a long, wide, dirty-water pipe leading straight up to the Citadel. Antenor's wife Theano, warned what to expect, had drugged the temple servants; so that Diomedes and Odysseus met no trouble at all once they reached the top by a hard, filthy climb. To make sure that the servants were not shamming sleep, they cut their throats and then returned the same way. Theano lowered the Palladium down after them, and put a replica in its place.

Diomedes, being higher in rank, carried the Palladium strapped to his shoulders, but Odysseus, who wanted all the glory for himself, let him go ahead and then stealthily unsheathed his sword. The rising moon peered large and bright over a crest of Mount Ida, throwing the shadow of

Odysseus's upraised sword-arm in front of Diomedes. He spun around, drew his own sword, disarmed Odysseus, tied his hands behind him, and drove him forward with repeated kicks and blows. Back in the Council Hut, Odysseus protested violently against Diomedes's treatment. He claimed to have unsheathed his sword because he heard a Trojan coming in pursuit. Agamemnon counted too much on Odysseus's help not to agree that Diomedes must have been mistaken.

Athene now inspired Odysseus to think of a stratagem for getting armed men into Troy. Under his directions, Epeius the Phocian, the best carpenter in camp though a fearful coward, built an enormous hollow horse out of fir planks. It had a concealed trap-door fitted into the left flank, and on the right a sentence carved in tall letters: 'With thankful hope of a safe return to their homes after nine years' absence, the Greeks dedicate this offering to Athene.' Odysseus would enter the horse by means of a rope-ladder, followed by Menelaus, Diomedes, Achilles's son Neoptolemus, and by eighteen more volunteers. Coaxed, threatened and bribed, Epeius was forced to sit by the trap door, which he alone could open quickly and silently.

Having gathered all their gear together, the Greeks set fire to their huts, launched the ships, and rowed off; but no farther than the other side of Tenedos, where they were invisible from Troy. Odysseus's companions already filled the horse, and only one Greek was left in the camp: his cousin Sinon.

When Trojan scouts went out at dawn they found the horse towering over the burned camp. Antenor knew nothing about the horse and therefore kept quiet, but King Priam and several of his sons wanted to bring it into the city on rollers. Others shouted: 'Athene has favoured the

Greeks far too long! Let her do what she pleases with her property.' Priam would listen neither to their protests nor to Aeneas's urgent warnings.

The horse had been purposely built too large for Troy's gates, and stuck four times even when these were removed and some stones pulled away from the wall on one side. With strenuous efforts the Trojans hauled it up to the Citadel, but at least took the precaution of re-building the wall and putting the gates back on their hinges. Priam's daughter Cassandra, whose curse was that no Trojan would ever take her prophecies seriously, screamed: 'Beware: the horse is full of armed men!'

Meanwhile two soldiers came across Sinon, hiding in a turret by the camp gate, and marched him to the Royal Palace. Asked why he had stayed behind, he told King Priam: 'I was afraid to sail in the same ship as my cousin Odysseus. He has long wanted to kill me, and yesterday nearly succeeded.'

'Why should Odysseus want to kill you?' asked Priam.

'Because I alone know how he got Palamedes stoned, and he doesn't trust my discretion. The fleet would have sailed a month ago, if the weather hadn't been so bad. Calchas of course prophesied, just as he did at Aulis, that a human sacrifice was needed, and Odysseus said: "Name the victim, please!" Calchas refused an immediate answer, but some days later (bribed, I suppose, by Odysseus) he named me. I was on the point of being sacrificed, when a favourable wind sprang up, I escaped in the excitement, and off they went.'

Priam believed Sinon's tale, freed him and asked for an explanation of the horse. Sinon answered: 'You remember those two temple servants who were found mysteriously murdered on the Citadel? That was Odysseus's work. He came by night, drugged the priestesses, and stole the Palladium. If you don't trust me, look carefully at what you think is the Palladium. You'll find that it's only a replica. Odysseus's theft made Athene so angry that the real Palladium, hidden in Agamemnon's hut, sweated as a warning of disaster. Calchas had a huge horse built in her honour, and warned Agamemnon to sail home.'

'Why was it made so huge!' asked Priam.

'To prevent it from being brought into the city. Calchas prophesied that if you succeeded in this, you could then raise an immense expedition from all over Asia Minor, invade Greece, and sack Agamemnon's own city of Mycenae.'

A Trojan nobleman named Laocoön interrupted Sinon by shouting: 'My lord King, these are certainly lies put into Sinon's mouth by Odysseus. Otherwise Agamemnon would have left the Palladium behind as well as the horse.' He added: 'And by the way, my lord, may I suggest that we sacrifice a bull to Poseidon—whose priest you stoned nine years ago because he refused to welcome Queen Helen?'

'I don't agree with you about the horse,' said Priam. 'But now that the war has ended, let us by all means regain Poseidon's favour. He treated us cruelly enough while it lasted.'

Laocoön went off to build an altar near the camp, and chose a young and healthy bull for sacrifice. He was preparing to strike it down with his axe, when a couple of immense monsters crawled from the sea and, twining around Laocoön's limbs and those of the two sons who were helping him, crushed the life out of them. The monsters then glided up to the Citadel, and there bowed their heads in honour of Athene—a sight which Priam unfortunately took to mean that Sinon had told the truth, and that Laocoön had been killed for contradicting him. In fact, however, Poseidon sent the sea-beasts at Athene's request: as a proof that he hated the Trojans as much as she did.

Priam dedicated the horse to Athene, and although Aeneas led his men safely away from Troy, suspecting any gift of the Greeks and refusing to believe the war ended—everyone else began victory celebrations. Trojan women visited the Scamander for the first time in nine years, gathering flowers by its banks to decorate the horse's wooden mane. They also spread a carpet of roses around its hooves. A tremendous banquet was got ready at Priam's palace.

Meanwhile, inside the horse, few of the Greeks could stop trembling. Epeius wept silently in utter terror, but Odysseus held a sword against his ribs, and if he had heard so much as a sigh would have driven it home. That evening, Helen strolled along and took a closer look at the horse. She reached up to pat its flanks and, as though to amuse Deiphobus who came with her, teased the hidden occupants by mimicking the voices of all their wives in turn. Not being a Trojan, she knew that Cassandra always spoke the truth; and also guessed which of the Greek leaders would have volunteered for this dangerous task. Diomedes and two others were tempted to answer 'Here I am!' when they heard their names spoken, but Odysseus restrained them and even had to strangle one man in the process.

Worn out by drinking and dancing, the Trojans slept soundly, and not even the bark of a dog broke the stillness. Helen alone lay awake, listening. At midnight, just before the full moon rose, the seventh of the year, Sinon crept from the city to light a beacon on Achilles's tomb; and Antenor waved a torch from the battlements. Agamemnon, whose ship lay anchored close offshore, replied to these signals by lighting a brazier filled with chips of pinewood. The whole fleet then quietly landed.

Antenor, tip-toeing up to the wooden horse, said in low tones: 'All's well! You may come out.' Epeius unlocked the trap door so noiselessly that someone fell through and broke his neck. The rest climbed down the rope-ladder. Two men went to open the City gates for Agamemnon; others murdered the sleeping sentries. But Menelaus could think only of Helen and, followed by Odysseus, ran at full speed towards Deiphobus's house.

CHAPTER ELEVEN

*

THE SACK OF TROY

Odysseus had undertaken to spare the life of any Trojans who offered no resistance; but, while respecting Antenor's mansion, on the door of which was chalked a leopard's skin design, his companions silently broke into all other houses and stabbed their occupants as they slept. Agamemnon's troops followed the example. Hecuba and her daughter fled to a sacred laurel-tree which overhung Almighty Zeus's altar. She kept tight hold of old Priam's arm to prevent him from fighting. It was only when Neoptolemus ran up and butchered their youngest child, splashing the altar with blood, that Priam broke away and seized a spear. Neoptolemus at once speared him and dragged his headless corpse off to Achilles's tomb, where he left it to rot unburied.

Prince Deiphobus, who was a magnificent swordsman,

struggled for his life against Odysseus and Menelaus on the stairs of his palace, and would have killed them both, had Helen not stolen quietly down and stabbed her hated new husband between the shoulders. Menelaus, though intending to cut Helen's throat, realized that she still loved him and, sheathing his sword, led her safely back to the ships.

Cassandra stood in Athene's temple clutching the wooden replica of the stolen Palladium. Little Ajax caught her by the hair, crying: 'Come, slave!' But she clung so tightly to the image that he had to bring it along, too. Later in the day, Agamemnon claimed Cassandra as his prize of honour and, to please him, Odysseus put the story about that Little Ajax had grossly insulted Athene by mishandling her priestess. To avoid being stoned to death, like Palamedes, Little Ajax took refuge at Athene's own altar and swore that Odysseus was lying once more. Nevertheless, Athene herself punished Little Ajax's violence: for when his ship was wrecked on the way home to Greece, she borrowed one of Almighty Zeus's thunderbolts and struck him dead as he scrambled ashore.

Agamemnon's people plundered Troy for three days and nights. Then they divided the spoils, burned the houses, pulled down the walls, and sacrificed immense numbers of cattle and sheep to the Olympians. Andromache had been given as a slave to Achilles's son Neoptolemus; and the Council discussed what should be done with young Scamandrius. Odysseus recommended the wiping out of all Priam's descendants, on the grounds that Heracles made the Trojan War possible by foolishly sparing Priam at the same age; and Calchas obligingly prophesied that Scamandrius, if left alive, would avenge his father and grandfather. Since everyone else shrank from so horrible a deed, Odysseus grimly flung the child over the battlements.

The Council also discussed Polyxena's fate. Calchas's view was that she should be sacrificed at Achilles's tomb, in accordance with his dying wish. Agamemnon protested. 'Enough blood has been spilt—the blood of old men and infants, as well as of fighters. Dead princes, however famous, have no claim upon the living.' But two Greek Councillors who had not got as much treasure as they hoped at the distribution of spoils, shouted that Agamemnon said this only to please Polyxena's sister Cassandra, and make her a more submissive prisoner. After a good deal of heated argument, Odysseus forced Agamemnon to give way. Polyxena was therefore slaughtered on Achilles's tomb, in sight of the whole army. Young Neoptolemus beheaded her with an axe. 'May you meet the same fate as I!' were her last words.

Favourable winds sprang up, and the Greek fleet was soon ready for launching. 'Off we sail at once, while the breeze holds!' cried Menelaus.

'No, no,' said Agamemnon. 'We must first sacrifice to Athene.'

'I owe the Goddess nothing,' grumbled Menelaus. 'She defended the Trojan Citadel against us far too long!'

The brothers parted on bad terms, and never saw each other again.

It remained to murder Polydorus, a child of Hecuba's old age, sent by her, a few years before, to safety in Thrace, where King Polymnestor reared him as though he were his son. Agamemnon's envoys now required Polymnestor to kill the boy, offering as payment a vast sum in gold and the hand of his daughter Electra. Fearing that to refuse would mean disaster, Polymnestor accepted the gold but, rather than break faith with Hecuba and Priam, killed his own son, Polydorus's playmate, in the envoys' presence. Seeing the King and Queen plunged in grief, and not knowing the secret of his own birth, Polydorus was so mystified by the murder that he went to consult the Delphic oracle. He asked Apollo's priestess: 'What troubles my parents?' She answered: 'Why are you not troubled yourself? Is it a small thing that your city has been burned, your father left unburied, your mother enslaved?' Polydorus returned in anxiety to Thrace, where he found nothing changed since his departure. 'Can Apollo be mistaken?' he wondered. Then the Queen told him who his parents really were.

Hecuba had indeed been enslaved by Odysseus. He was about to sail off with her, but she heaped such hideous curses on him and the other cruel, lying, treacherous Greek leaders, that he decided to kill her. However, she transformed herself by magic into a fearful black bitch, and ran around howling so dismally that everyone fled in terror and confusion.

Antenor never became King of Troy as he had been promised, nor got any share in the spoils; but Menelaus generously took him, his wife Theano, and their four surviving sons aboard his ship. They settled first in North Africa, then in Thrace, and finally colonized the islands of Henetica, now Venice. He also founded the town of Padua. The one other Trojan hero who escaped was Aeneas: from Dardanus, his city near Mount Ida, he had seen the distant flames of Troy and, crossing the Hellespont, took refuge in Thrace. The Romans say he eventually wandered to Italy, and there became Julius Caesar's ancestor.

Troy lost its importance, since the Greeks were at last able to enter the Black Sea freely and trade with the East. A few landless, houseless folk settled in the city ruins. Aeneas's grandson Ascanius ruled them; but it was a poor kingdom. And a generation later, Zeus taking Hera at her word, destroyed the three cities, Mycenae, Argos and Sparta, which she loved best.

Calchas travelled southward through Asia Minor to Colophon, where he died (as an oracle had warned him) on meeting a rival who could foretell the future better than himself. This was Apollo's son Mopsus. A large fig-tree grew at Colophon, and Calchas tried to shame Mopsus by challenging him: 'Can you perhaps tell me, dear fellow-prophet, how many figs grow on that tree?' Mopsus, closing his eyes, because he trusted to inner sight rather than to calculation, answered: 'Certainly: first ten thousand figs, then a bushel of figs according to the measure used in Aegina, carefully weighed–and, yes, one single fig left over.' Calchas laughed scornfully at the extra fig; but when the tree had been stripped, and the fruit weighed and counted, Mopsus proved exactly right.

'To come down from thousands to lesser quantities, dear fellow-prophet,' said Mopsus. 'Can you perhaps tell me how many piglings that fat sow will produce, and when they'll be born, and of what sex they'll be?'

'Eight piglings, all male, and she'll have them within nine days,' answered Calchas at random, hoping to have left Colophon before his guess could be checked.

'I believe that you're in error,' said Mopsus, again closing his eyes. 'I prophesy that she'll have no more than three piglings, only one of them male, and that they'll be born at midnight tomorrow, not a minute earlier.'

Mopsus was right, and Calchas died of shame–Apollo's punishment for the many bad guesses he had made to please Agamemnon and Odysseus.

CHAPTER TWELVE

*

THE GREEKS GO HOME

The Greeks who sailed off had aroused the anger of so many powerful gods and goddesses that they soon heartily wished themselves back before Troy.

Menelaus, caught in a storm sent by Athene to punish his insult, lost all the large Spartan fleet, except five ships. These were blown to Crete, and from Crete to Egypt. He spent eight years in Southern waters, because whenever he tried to sail home, a new storm blew his ships ashore again. Yet Athene let him visit Cyprus, Phoenicia, Ethiopia and Libya where, on Helen's account, he was hospitably received at every royal court; for, though well past the age of child-bearing, she continued to entrance all who set eyes on her.

Eighteen years' absence from Sparta numbed Menelaus's heart; but at last he landed on the Egyptian island of Pharos, and there heard that his one hope of getting back lay in capturing Proteus, a prophetic Sea-god who shepherded a great flock of seals, and demanding his advice. Menelaus and three friends accordingly killed three seals out of thousands that they found crowding the beach and, putting on their flayed skins, concealed themselves among the flock. When after a while Proteus swam up and unsuspectingly took a nap beside them, they tied him fast with a chain. He changed into various shapes—a lion, a serpent, a panther, a wild boar, running water, and a leafy bush—but could not get free. 'Speak!' ordered Menelaus. 'Teach me to break the spell that keeps us from returning home!' 'Have you tried offering Athene sacrifices?' asked Proteus. Somehow Menelaus had never thought of this. He sailed to Egypt and did as Proteus advised. At once the winds blew fair, and he arrived at Sparta safely ten days later.

It will be remembered how Nauplius had avenged his murdered son Palamedes—he went around Greece warning the wives of Palamedes's enemies that their husbands planned to divorce them and marry beautiful Trojan captives. Most of these Queens believed Nauplius and took lovers who would seize the throne and protect them against such a disgrace. When Agamemnon reached Mycenae, rescued by Athene from a storm that sank half his fleet, Clytaemnestra came out to greet him as a conquering hero. She knew of his arrival well in advance, because he had arranged to light a beacon on Mount Ida as soon as Troy fell and have ready a whole chain of beacons to carry the news to Mycenae by way of Lemnos and Thrace.

Clytaemnestra thought that Cassandra, who followed in Agamemnon's train, was to be his new Queen; she unrolled a purple carpet and led Agamemnon to a luxurious bath-house in the middle of the palace courtyard, where slave-girls were preparing warm water. But Cassandra refused to enter the court, falling into a prophetic trance and screaming: 'I smell blood! I smell blood!' After a pleasant wash, Agamemnon put one foot out of the bath and Clytaemnestra gave him an apple to eat. He set it to his lips; she threw a net over his head; he struggled to escape. Then Clytaemnestra's lover Aegisthus, broadsword in hand, stole up and struck him twice between neck and shoulder. Agamemnon fell back into the bath, where Clytaemnestra cut off his head with an axe. Then she ran away and did the same to Cassandra.

The home-coming Greeks attacked Aegisthus's guards, but at the close of a bitter struggle, none were left alive. Agamemnon's strange end fulfilled a prophecy known to Clytaemnestra: that he would die neither inside the palace, nor outside—the bath-house in the courtyard made good this part of the prophecy; neither on water nor on land—he had one foot in the bath, the other on the floor; neither dressed nor undressed—the net was not clothing, though it covered his body; neither feasting nor fasting—he had set an apple to his lips but not yet eaten it.

Aegisthus killed two of Agamemnon's three sons by Clytaemnestra. The third son survived—ten-year-old Orestes, whom a noble-hearted nurse rescued. She put her own son to bed in the royal nursery, and let Aegisthus smother him with sheets. Orestes was meanwhile smuggled out of the palace by his sister Electra; and a kind friend of the family, reigning near Delphi, adopted him. Aegisthus ruled at Mycenae for seven years. He would have killed Electra too, fearing she might become the wife of some king, and one day tell her children to avenge their famous grandfather's

death. But Clytaemnestra stopped Aegisthus: 'No,' she said, 'I'll marry her to a peasant, instead, and keep a careful eye on her.' This was done. However, Electra often sent Orestes secret messages, reminding him of his duty to murder Aegisthus.

At the age of seventeen, Orestes consulted the Delphic oracle. The priestess replied that unless he did as his sister asked, Apollo would make him a leper; yet recommended the greatest caution. Orestes therefore went with his friend Pylades to the palace at Mycenae, pretending to be a pedlar, and telling Aegisthus that a stranger on the Delphi road had given him bad news for Queen Clytaemnestra: her son Orestes was dead of a fever. 'The man I met,' Orestes said, 'will soon arrive, bringing the ashes in a brass urn.' Neither Clytaemnestra nor Aegisthus recognized Orestes, and half an hour later Pylades came in and gave them a brass urn, supposedly containing the ashes. They felt much relieved to be safe from vengeance. But as the four of them stood chatting, Orestes drew his sword and killed Aegisthus. According to some accounts, he also killed Clytaemnestra. The truth, however, seems to be that he merely handed her over to a court of justice; and that when they pronounced sentence of death, he excused himself from recommending her to mercy, as he might have done, being now High King of Greece.

King Idomeneus made a miserable return to Crete. His wife, Queen Meda, had chosen one Leucus as her lover. Leucus usurped the throne, but then murdered Meda and most of her family, arguing that if she could deceive Idomeneus, she might equally deceive him. Only Meda's youngest daughter escaped to a wild part of the island where, as it happened, Idomeneus's small fleet was driven by a storm. He vowed to Poseidon that if he came safely ashore, he would sacrifice the first living thing who met him. This proved to be his own daughter, and Idomeneus was on the point of fulfilling the vow, when suddenly a plague broke out among his men, and he laid down the axe. Leucus, hearing the story, blamed Idomeneus not only for failing to keep his vow but for causing the plague. Banished from Crete, Idomeneus emigrated to Calabria in Southern Italy, where he died some years later.

King Diomedes, reaching Argos with a score or two of followers, learned that his wife, too, had been unfaithful, and that her lover had usurped the throne. Driven out by his former subjects, he followed Idomeneus to Italy, and built the famous city of Brundisium, now Brindisi.

According to the oldest account, even worse fortune overtook Odysseus, who deserved far harsher punishment than the other Greek leaders. Back in Ithaca, after a disastrous ten-year voyage, he came upon his wife Penelope, entertaining not one, but fifty, lovers! Odysseus sailed in disgust to Aetolia, where he spent ten further years of misery. When eventually he returned, his son Telemachus, mistaking him for a pirate, ran him through with a sting-ray spear as he leaped ashore.

Teucer the Archer fetched his small fleet safely home to Salamis, yet old King Telamon took an army down to the beach and would not let him land. 'Why haven't you avenged your glorious brother Ajax, by killing Agamemnon and Odysseus?' he asked sternly. 'Why haven't you at least brought me my son's bones?' Teucer could only shrug in reply; so, despite his mother Hesione's tears and protests, he was forced to sail off again. Cyprus seemed a suitable place of exile, and there he met a warmer welcome. Having married the King's daughter, he founded a new city, also called Salamis, and never returned home, even for Telamon's funeral.

Neoptolemus reached Phthia in safety, and afterwards became the husband of Hermione, Helen's daughter by Menelaus. He was rash enough, however, to visit Delphi and there accuse Apollo of having disguised himself as Paris and shot his father Achilles. When the priestess coldly denied the truth of this charge, Neoptolemus plundered and burned the temple. He reappeared a few years later, and now accused Apollo of making Hermione barren. The priestess ordered him to sacrifice some fat cattle to the God. Neoptolemus obeyed, yet stopped the temple servant as he began hauling the beef away, and kept it for himself. 'Who will avenge Polyxena and rid us of this troublesome young fellow?' cried the priestess. 'Count upon me,' answered the temple servant. He chopped Neoptolemus down with his sacrificial axe, and buried the body under the threshold of Apollo's newly-rebuilt temple. Polyxena was thus avenged.

According to another account, Orestes bribed the Delphians to kill Neoptolemus, having been promised Hermione in marriage before ever Menelaus went to Troy. There may be truth in this story, too.

The one Greek leader who could not regret his homecoming was King Nestor. He had taken no active part in the Trojan War, being already too much of a veteran to do more than drive shouting about the battlefield; and though his advice usually proved bad, had broken no oaths, offended no gods, deceived no friends, and committed no murders. He found all well at Sandy Pylos, and enjoyed a peaceful old age, surrounded by brave, obedient sons, who listened attentively while he told and re-told anecdotes of his exploits in long-forgotten campaigns.

CHAPTER THIRTEEN

*

ODYSSEUS'S WANDERINGS

According to the *Odyssey,* a poem that shows Odysseus in a different light, he first sailed for Thrace after leaving Troy. There he plundered and burned the city-port of Ismarus. A priest of Apollo, whose life he undertook to spare, gratefully gave him several jars of sweet wine, half of which his men drank at a picnic on the beach. Some Thracians who lived inland saw flames rising from Ismarus, and charged vengefully down on the drunken sailors. Odysseus got most of these aboard again, though he had to abandon his dead and seriously wounded. A fierce north-easterly gale then drove his fleet across the Aegean Sea towards Cythera, an island at the southernmost point of Greece. Taking advantage of a sudden lull, he made his men use their oars and tried to round Cythera, bearing north-west for Ithaca, but the gale sprang up more fiercely than before, and blew nine days. When at last it dropped, Odysseus found himself within sight of Syrinx, the Lotus-eaters' island off the North African coast.

The lotus is a sweet, stoneless, yellow cherry, and wholesome enough, apart from making all who eat it lose their memories. Odysseus went ashore on Syrinx, and while he filled his water jars, sent out three scouts to see what food could be bought or seized. The scouts having eaten several lotuses offered them by friendly natives, at once forgot where they were and why they had come, and even their own names. After waiting several hours, Odysseus headed a rescue party and brought the scouts back in chains. They had wanted nothing better than to spend the rest of their lives there, eating lotuses.

Odysseus steered north till he reached a fertile but uninhabited island off Sicily, full of wild goats, some of which he shot for food. He then took a single ship to explore the opposite coast. This was the land of the fierce Cyclopes, or Round-eyes, so called because each had a glaring round eye in the middle of his forehead. The Cyclopes were gigantic shepherds, living sullenly apart from one another in rocky caves. Odysseus and his companions saw the high, ivy-covered entrance to one such cavern behind a large sheep-pen. They entered, unaware that it was the home of Polyphemus, a man-eating Cyclops. Finding nobody about, they lit a fire, killed and roasted some kids that ran up, helped themselves to cheese from baskets hanging on the walls, and fed happily. Towards evening, Polyphemus arrived. He drove his flock into the cave and closed the mouth with a stone so huge that thirty teams of oxen could scarcely have stirred it. Some minutes later, as Polyphemus sat milking his sheep and goats, he glanced up and saw Odysseus. 'What's your business?' he asked gruffly. 'We are Greeks, fresh from the famous sack of Troy,' answered Odysseus, 'and trusting to your hospitality.'

Polyphemus at once took two sailors, smashed their heads on the rocky floor, and ate them raw. Odysseus refrained from attacking the monster; since he and his companions were not nearly strong enough to unblock the entrance, they could hardly hope to escape by killing him. At breakfast time, Polyphemus ate two more sailors, then rolled away the stone, drove out his flock, and rolled the stone back into place.

Odysseus found a stake of green olive, sharpened one end with his sword, and hid it under a mound of sheep droppings. On his return that evening, Polyphemus again ate two more sailors. Odysseus, who had brought a skin of wine ashore, offered him a bowlful. The monster drank greedily, never having tasted wine before, and demanded another pint. 'What's your name?' he asked. 'My name is Nobody,' Odysseus answered, pouring the wine. 'Then I'll promise to eat you last, dear Nobody! I like your wine. Make it two pints next time!'

Soon he fell into a drunken sleep. Odysseus set fire to the pointed end of his stake and drove it into Polyphemus's eye, twisting it around. The eye hissed, Polyphemus yelled, and all the other Cyclopes, hearing the hubbub, gathered outside the cave. 'What's wrong, neighbour?' they shouted.

'Help! I'm blinded and in agony! It's Nobody's fault,' he shouted back.

'Poor fellow! If it's nobody's fault, there's nothing more to be said. Good-bye, and please make less noise!'

Polyphemus crawled to the cave-mouth and groped around, in the hope of catching a sailor or two; but the firelight helped them to avoid him. At dawn, Odysseus tied each of his companions in turn face upwards underneath the belly of a sheep, the middle one of three. 'Keep the others in line by gripping their fleeces,' he ordered. Odysseus himself chose the biggest ram of all, and when Polyphemus let the flock out to pasture, stroking their backs to make sure that nobody was astride them, he curled up underneath this ram, hanging on by his fingers and toes. Polyphemus stopped the big ram and talked long and sadly to him, not realizing how near his enemy was. So Odysseus and the surviving sailors escaped, and got the whole flock aboard their ship. As they sailed off, yelling taunts, Polyphemus threw three immense rocks, but missed each time.

Odysseus now steered past Sicily to the island of King Aeolus, divine Guardian of the Winds. Here he was entertained nobly for a month; after which Aeolus gave him a leather bag, its neck secured by silver wire. 'I have imprisoned all my winds in this bag,' he said, 'except the gentle West Wind. He'll blow you across the sea to Ithaca. But if you change your course, open the bag with care and summon whichever wind you need.'

The ship had come so close to Ithaca that smoke could be seen rising from the fires of the royal palace, when Odysseus fell asleep, utterly exhausted. His men, expecting the leather bag to contain wine, untied the silver wire and opened it wide. Out roared the winds in a body, driving the ship before them! Less than an hour had passed when Odysseus found himself on King Aeolus's island again, apologizing and pleading for further help. Aeolus refused. 'Use your oars!' he cried sharply.

Odysseus's men rowed off, and next day came to Formiae, a land-locked Italian port, inhabited by the cannibal Laestrygones. He beached his fleet and sent a few sailors off to fetch water. But, gathering on the ring of cliffs above, the Laestrygones hurled boulders which smashed his ships to pieces. Then they murdered and ate the crews. Odysseus escaped in a single ship.

A fierce southerly gale now blew him to the very top of the Adriatic Sea, and he landed at Aeaea, a small island ruled by the Goddess Circe. When Odysseus's friend Eurylochus took a party of twenty-two men ashore, Circe invited them all to her palace. Wolves and lions prowled around the garden. To Eurylochus's surprise, instead of attacking the sailors, they stood on their hindlegs and fondly caressed them.

Circe gave her visitors a fine banquet, consisting of cheese, barley bread, honey and wine; but it was drugged. They had eaten only a few mouthfuls when she struck them on the shoulder with her wand. They turned into pigs, which she shut in a filthy sty, throwing acorns after them for dessert. Those lions and wolves were also men, similarly enchanted. Eurylochus alone got away—he had been afraid of a trap and, instead of entering the palace, peered through a window.

Odysseus seized his sword and hurried to the rescue. On the way he met Hermes, who kindly gave him a charm against Circe's magic: a highly-scented white flower with a black root, called *moly*.

Circe set the same sort of meal before Odysseus, but when she waved her wand to transform him, he smelt the moly flower, took no harm, and threatened to chop her head off. Circe fell weeping at his feet. Odysseus spared her on condition that she restored all the animals to human shape, and never used such wicked charms again. They grew very friendly, and spent three years together as man and wife.

Circe helped Odysseus to visit the Underworld, where he exchanged news with the ghosts of Agamemnon, Achilles and other old comrades—Great Ajax alone scowled and went angrily away. Odysseus then said good-bye to Circe, promising to be back soon, and sailed south for Ithaca. Circe had warned him against Siren Island. The Sirens were half-bird, half-woman, and sang so beautifully that sailors who heard their voices always tried to steer towards them, but wrecked their vessels on hidden rocks guarding the shore. Though Odysseus stopped his sailors' ears with wax and made them lash him to the mast, he heard the Sirens' songs as the ship went by. 'Release me,' he shouted, 'or I'll kill everyone of you!' Since the sailors could not hear either the Sirens or Odysseus, they obeyed his earlier order by lashing him still more tightly to the mast. Their ship thus escaped disaster, and the Sirens committed suicide in vexation.

Presently Odysseus had to steer between two steep cliffs separating Italy from Sicily. On the Sicilian side lived Charybdis, a monster who three times a day swallowed huge masses of water, which she then suddenly spurted out in the form of a whirlpool. On the Italian side lived Scylla, a six-headed bitch who ate sailors. Edging away from her, to avoid the worse danger of Charybdis, Odysseus lost a quarter of his crew: Scylla leaned over, snatching two sailors in each pair of jaws and devouring them at leisure.

Next day he landed in Sicily, to wait for a favourable wind; but Circe's provisions had all been eaten, and the sailors grew hungry. While Odysseus slept, they shot and roasted some cows owned by the Sun-god Hyperion, who made a complaint to Almighty Zeus. As they sailed on again, Zeus hurled his thunderbolt at the ship and sank her. Everyone drowned, except Odysseus. He clung to the broken mast and, after nine days of drifting, was cast ashore on Calypso's island, famished and barely alive.

Calypso, a beautiful sorceress, at once fell in love with Odysseus, and kept him five years more. He soon wearied of her company, there being nobody else about, and would sit gloomily on the shore, all day long, gazing at the horizon. At last Zeus sent an order, which Calypso dared not disobey: 'Release King Odysseus!' She fetched an axe, a saw, and other tools from some hiding place, and told him to build a raft of tree-trunks. When it was finished, he kissed Calypso good-bye, put food aboard, launched the raft on rollers, set sail, and was driven forward by a gentle breeze. He had not gone any great distance before an immense wave overturned the raft, and Odysseus never discovered which god to blame for this disaster.

Two days later he was washed ashore, naked, near Drepane in Sicily, where the lovely Princess Nausicaa had taken her girls to wash clothes at a river mouth. While they were playing catch together in their midday break, the ball bounced into the water close to a thicket behind which Odysseus lay hidden. The girls shrieked as he came out, but Nausicaa lent him clothes and took him to the palace of her father, King Alcinous. After listening to Odysseus's not very truthful account of his adventures, Alcinous sent him to Ithaca in a fine ship. Yet again, on catching sight of his own island, Odysseus fell asleep.

The sailors did not dare wake Odysseus; instead, they laid him down on the beach and rowed away. He was woken up by Athene, disguised as a shepherd boy, and pretended to be a Cretan who had been put ashore against his will. Athene laughed. 'Never lie to a goddess!' she said. 'If you take my advice, you'll visit Eumaeus, your old swineherd, and hear the latest news. He can be trusted.'

Odysseus duly revealed himself to Eumaeus, and learned that one hundred and twelve insolent young noblemen were courting his wife Penelope, and feasting every day in the palace at her expense. 'They threaten to stay until she decides which of them to marry,' Eumaeus explained. 'But Queen Penelope knows from an oracle that you're returning soon; so she's playing for time. She tells her suitors that they must wait while she finishes a difficult piece of embroidery. Although working all day, she unpicks the stitches at night, month after month.'

Dressed in old rags like a beggar, Odysseus went to the palace, and there saw Argus, his old hunting dog, crouched on a dung heap, mangy, decrepit, and tormented by fleas, yet still alive. Argus wagged his hairless stump of a tail, and died happily; Odysseus wiped away a tear. In the courtyard he walked round the tables, begging Penelope's suitors to give him scraps of food. None offered him any; one even threw a foot-stool at his head. Then Irus, a real beggar, tried to chase him away and, when he stood fast, challenged him to a boxing match but got knocked down with a single blow.

Meanwhile Odysseus's son Telemachus came back from a journey. Stopping at Eumaeus's hut, he heard that the suitors were plotting to murder him, and that his father had just arrived in disguise. The three soon got together and planned how to punish the suitors. When Odysseus visited Penelope, she did not recognize him; so he told her a long tale about having met her husband on his way to Zeus's oracle at Dodona. 'He'll be here within a few days,' Odysseus said.

Penelope listened eagerly, and ordered Eurycleia, a very old servant who had been Odysseus's nurse, to wash the noble stranger's feet. As Penelope left the room, Eurycleia recognized a scar on his leg and uttered a cry of joy; but Odysseus gripped her by the throat and made her keep silence, not yet certain whether Penelope could be trusted.

The following afternoon, on Telemachus's advice, Penelope announced to the suitors that she would marry the one who succeeded in sending an arrow through the rings of twelve axes set upright in a straight row. (These rings were used for hanging the axes on walls.) Everyone must shoot with Odysseus's own bow, she said.

They all wanted to string the bow, which was so stiff from twenty years' disuse that none could bend it. At last Odysseus, despite many protests and vulgar insults, seized the bow, strung it easily, and his arrow flew clean through the row of rings.

Telemachus, having quietly slipped away, now re-entered brandishing a sword. Odysseus at once shot the chief suitor in the throat. His companions jumped up to snatch spears from the walls, but Telemachus had removed these the night before. Odysseus's arrows felled the suitors in heaps; and Telemachus, helped by Eumaeus and another armed palace servant, got rid of the rest. It was only afterwards that Odysseus revealed himself to Penelope.

The same gallant four men fought a hard battle next day against the suitors' relatives, and were close to winning a second victory, when Athene flew down and imposed a truce.

Odysseus then ruled Ithaca in peace until he died.

INDEX

INDEX